advanced applied science

AQA A2 GCE UNIT 8

medical physics

science

advanced applied science
AQA A2 GCE UNIT 8
medical physics

Publisher

4science

6 The Courtyard, Dean's Farm

Phillips Lane, Stratford sub Castle

Salisbury

Wiltshire, SP1 3YP

www.4science.org.uk

Images

Photos.com [Jupiter Images]

(unless otherwise stated)

Printed in Great Britain

JMD Print Management Limited

3 Mile's Buildings, George Street, Bath, BA1 2QS

A catalogue record for this book is available from the British Library

ISBN 978-0-9557841-2-5

writing and editing

4science

The 4science team and its associates are experienced teachers, examiners and curriculum developers.

They are led by Ken Gadd who has extensive experience in developing qualifications and learning materials. He has authored a number of science textbooks.

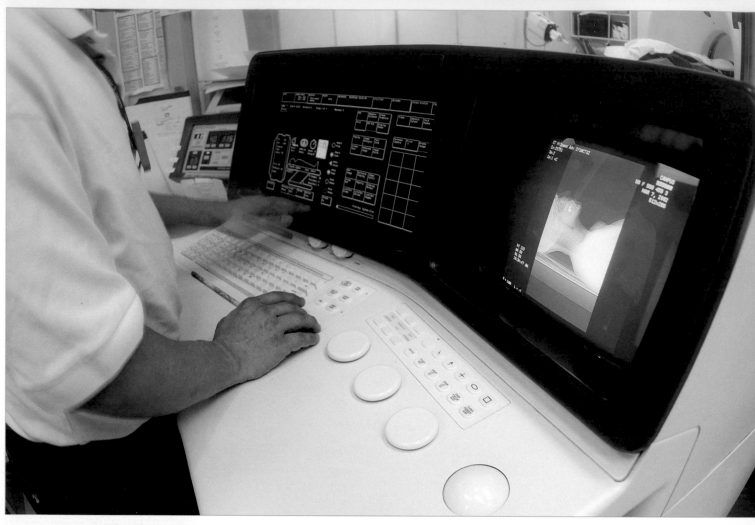

About the book

This revision guide contains a series of double page spreads. On each spread there are questions to answer, crosswords to complete or diagrams to label.

When there's something to do, instructions are written in *italics in this colour*.

There are a few ruled pages at the back of the book which you can use to scribble answers and other notes. You'll probably find it useful to work through the book with some extra paper, too, so you can answer longer questions. Write down any working so you can trace any mistakes.

We've **highlighted** the important words. Make sure you know what they mean. As you write your revision notes, you may find it useful to create your own glossary.

About the exam

In this unit you will be required to complete an external examination of 1½ hours duration. The examination will consist of a series of compulsory short answer, structured questions and will be marked out of 80.

You will be assessed on your knowledge, understanding and skills relating to medical physics.

You should ensure that you have a detailed knowledge and understanding of all the information in *The specification*.

You should be able to plan and evaluate investigations ensuring that they are valid and reliable. This is for investigations in the laboratory context, and from the point of view of professionals working in a scientific environment.

You will need to be able to recall, use and manipulate all the formulae contained in this book.

To gain high marks in the examination you should:

*   be familiar with all the content described in the unit
*   be able to apply the knowledge you have learned to familiar and unfamiliar situations
*   ensure that your answers meet the requirements specified in each question
*   avoid irrelevance
*   write answers which are logical and coherent paying particular attention to correct spelling, punctuation and grammar.

Contents

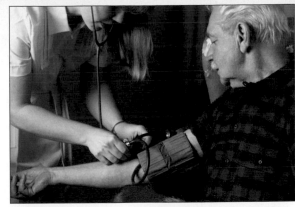

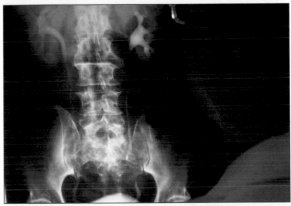

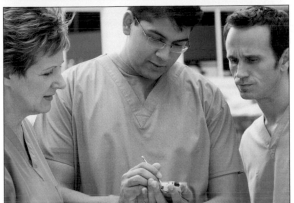

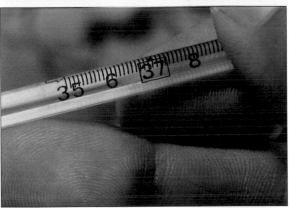

What you need to know ...

The following four pages use text taken from the AQA specification. The bullet points outline what you should know, understand and be able to demonstrate in your exam. There's a blank box for you to tick as and when you've revised each bullet point. Topics are not covered in exactly the same order as the specification – so you might find it useful to make a note of the page number for each relevant bullet point. Hopefully, you'll agree that any change in order is a logical change, making it easier for you to follow!

You need to know, understand and be able to demonstrate ...

How physiological measurements are indicators of health

Healthcare professionals use a variety of techniques to assess and monitor the health of patients.

You should learn how to measure the following:	revised?
• body temperature*	
• blood pressure	
• heart activity	
• brain activity	

*For body temperature measurements you should know about commonly used thermometers (liquid-in-glass clinical thermometers and thermistor thermometers) in terms of how they work and the advantages and disadvantages of each type of thermometer for measuring and monitoring core body temperature; you should also be able to evaluate the choice of thermometer and blood pressure monitor to perform a specified function

You should know the following and be able to apply this knowledge to a range of appropriate medical situations:	revised?
• the value of normal core body temperature and the range of core temperatures over which the body can survive, noting the effects on the body as the temperature moves from normal towards the lower and upper limits of this range. This should include the symptoms of hyperthermia and hypothermia	

• the range of body temperatures measured in the mouth
   • normal = 36.8 °C ; range 36.5-37.2 °C
   • death = below 25 °C
   • hypothermia = 32 °C
   • fever = above 37.2 °C
 • heat exhaustion or heat stroke = likely if above 38 °C in absence of infection
 • high temperatures that would lead to death = above 43 °C	

• the structure of a sphygmomanometer, how it works, how it is used and why blood pressure readings are taken at the upper arm	
• the terms *systolic* pressure and *diastolic* pressure, and be able to explain them and describe how the person using a sphygmomanometer can record these values of blood pressure	

How physiological measurements are indicators of health (continued ...)

• the difference between invasive and non-invasive methods of measuring blood pressure, and comment on the advantages and disadvantages of each evaluating their use in a variety of situations	
• the normal values of blood pressure for healthy young adult males (125/80 mm Hg) and healthy young adult females (123/80 mm Hg) and be able to explain what each figure represents and relates to	
• that an electrocardiogram (ECG) monitors heart activity, be able to recognise a normal ECG trace and describe how this trace changes during heart attack, sinus tachycardia, bradycardia and ventricular fibrillation. You should be able to explain why patients need to be relaxed and still while an ECG trace is being taken	
• that an electroencephalogram (EEG) monitors electrical activity of the brain. You should be able to draw typical traces for alpha, beta, delta and theta waves and know when each of these types of wave is produced	
• that EEGs are used to diagnose brain disorders, research sleep, monitor the effects of anaesthetics and provide evidence of brain death	

The use of diagnostic techniques

Healthcare professionals now have a wide range of sophisticated tools to assist them in diagnosis. Such tools make use of a wide range of scientific principles and allow healthcare professionals to be more accurate in their diagnosis.

You should know:	revised?
• how X-rays, radioactivity (alpha (α) particles, beta (β) particles and gamma (γ) rays), ultrasound, magnetic fields (MRI), thermography and endoscopy (using optical fibres) are used to diagnose a variety of conditions	
• the advantages and disadvantages of using each of the above	
• the type(s) of diagnostic tool(s) most suitable for diagnosing specific problems	

Thermography and its uses

Detection of infrared radiation emitted from the body is a useful non-invasive method of investigating possible illness.

You should:	revised?
• know how a thermograph is produced	
• know some situations where thermography is a good diagnostic tool and the advantages and disadvantages of using thermography	
• be able to evaluate the appropriate use of thermography for diagnosis in a variety of situations	

The use of X-rays

The use of X-rays to investigate inside the body without the need for surgery was one of the earliest of the modern diagnostic techniques. The dangers of X-rays were discovered some time after their original discovery and early use. Modern equipment, techniques and safety precautions have reduced the risk to patients and those who use X-rays.

You should know:	revised?
• that X-rays are high frequency electromagnetic waves	
• the dangers of using X-rays and how the extent of damage caused depends on the part of the body exposed, the dose received, the rate at which it is received, and the importance of using the lowest effective dose	
• the difference between stochastic and non-stochastic effects, the difference between hereditary and somatic effects and be familiar with the sievert (Sv) as the unit of dose equivalent	
• the precautions taken by radiographers when using X-rays to protect both themselves and the patient	
• how X-rays are produced – including the basic structure of an X-ray tube	
• how X-ray images are formed (exposure of photographic film) and the meaning of the terms *attenuation* and *contrast*	
• how contrast media can be used to enhance X-ray images	
• what CAT scans are, how they produce images and how they differ from standard X-rays	
• how CAT scans are similar to, and different from, MRI scans	
• some situations where X-rays are a good diagnostic technique and, by considering the different attenuation effects of different tissues, be able to explain why X-rays are suitable for diagnosing some conditions but not others	
• be able to evaluate the use of X-rays and CAT scans in specified situations	

Radiation, its uses and dangers

Radiation can be used for both diagnosis and treatment. Healthcare professionals need to consider the use to which radiation is to be put before deciding on the most appropriate type of radiation to use, the dosage and how it is to be applied.

You should know:	revised?
• that there are three types of radioactivity – alpha (α) particles, beta (β) particles and gamma (γ) rays	
• the different penetration powers of each of the three types of radioactivity and how these can be measured in the laboratory	
• the relative dangers of each type of radioactivity and the importance of using the lowest effective dose when using radioisotopes for diagnosis	

Radiation, its uses and dangers (continued ...)

• that radioactive decay is random	
• the concept of half-life and how it is measured – including graphical methods to represent radioactive decay and to calculate half-life, and methods to ensure that data is valid and reliable	
• how radioisotopes can be used for diagnosis and the factors affecting the choice of radioisotope – including explaining why radioisotopes used as tracers should ideally emit only gamma radiation	
• why certain radioisotopes – for example technetium-99 and iodine-131 – are commonly used. You should be aware of properties such as ease of manufacture, half-life, cost, type of radiation emitted and organ affinity	
• the precautions taken by radiographers and medical physicists when using radioisotopes and the scientific reasons for these precautions	
• how to detect radioactivity – including Geiger counters, gamma cameras, rectilinear scanners and film badges	
• why, in the body, radioisotopes have an effective half-life (T_E) which is shorter than their radioactive half-life (T_P) and how these are calculated by the use and manipulation of the formula $$\frac{1}{T_E} = \frac{1}{T_P} = \frac{1}{T_B}$$	
• how to plan, carry out and evaluate experiments related to radioactivity	

The uses of ultrasound

Ultrasound is a relatively modern technique for examining the inside of the human body without the need for surgery. It is mainly a diagnostic technique rather than a treatment.

You should know:	revised?
• what ultrasound is and how ultrasound images are produced	
• how ultrasound is used for diagnosis	
• in which situations ultrasound is a good diagnostic tool and in which it is unsuitable, and be able to evaluate the use of ultrasound in specified circumstances	
• how to describe ultrasonic waves in terms of velocity, frequency and wavelength. You should be able to use and manipulate the formula: velocity (v) = frequency (f) × wavelength (λ)	
• how and why the speed of ultrasonic waves is different in different materials	
• how ultrasound is absorbed, attenuated and reflected differently by different materials and how to use the formula: $$\left(\frac{Z_2 - Z_1}{Z_2 + Z_1}\right)^2$$ to calculate the intensity reflection coefficient, α, between two media	
• how to link the clarity and contrast of the ultrasound image formed and the need to use a gel as a coupling agent	

Lasers and fibre optics in medicine

We normally think of fibre optics as being used in mass communications, but their use in healthcare diagnosis is now well established.

You should know:	revised?
• how light, with particular reference to lasers, is transmitted along optical fibres	
• how optical fibres are used in diagnosis	
• situations where optical fibres are a suitable diagnostic tool	
• the advantages and disadvantages of using optical fibres for diagnosis compared with other diagnostic methods	
• how to calculate refractive index (n) and critical angle (c) using the formulae refractive index, $n = \dfrac{\sin i}{\sin r}$ $\quad \sin c = \dfrac{1}{n}$ and the significance of the values obtained	
• the principles behind cladding optical fibres	
• how to plan, carry out and evaluate investigations involving refractive index and total internal reflection	

Magnetic resonance imaging (MRI)

The use of MRI is becoming increasingly common as a diagnostic technique.

You should know:	revised?
• how MRI images are formed	
• about situations where MRI imaging is an appropriate technique and be able to evaluate the use of MRI in specified circumstances	
• the similarities and differences between MRI and CAT scans	

How radioisotopes, ultrasound and light are used in therapy

You should know:	revised?
• that radioisotopes, ultrasound and light are used in the treatment of various illnesses, and the advantages and disadvantages of each type of therapy	
• which type(s) of therapy would be most suitable for treating particular medical complaints	
• how ultrasound can be used for therapy – including medical complaints commonly treated with ultrasound (gall stones and kidney stones) – and the advantages and disadvantages of ultrasound as therapy compared with other methods for specific medical complaints	

How radioisotopes, ultrasound and light are used in therapy (continued ...)

You should know:	revised?
• how lasers can be used as surgical instruments, both alone and in conjunction with optical fibres	
• how optical fibres can be used in conjunction with miniature surgical equipment and/or lasers in keyhole surgery	
• the advantages and disadvantages of using lasers in surgery compared with traditional methods	
• the advantages and disadvantages of using keyhole surgery compared with traditional surgical methods	
• the dangers involved in using lasers in surgery and the precautions that need to be taken when they are in use	
• the factors affecting the choice of radioisotope for treatment of a particular medical complaint	

• the types of complaints normally treated with radiotherapy and the isotopes commonly used to treat specific tumours
   • cobalt-60 for general therapy
   • iridium-192 for breast cancer implants
   • iodine-131 for thyroid cancer	

• that the choice of radioisotope can depend on organ affinity, and be able to explain why the radioisotopes used inside the body for therapy are normally emitters of beta radiation	
• the factors to be taken into consideration when planning the treatment of a specified condition	
• how to evaluate the choice of specific therapeutic methods in the treatment of specified conditions	

time to revise

Waves 1

Two kinds of wave

A wave is moving energy, not material. There are two main types of wave:

Transverse waves are waves in which the displacement of the particles is at right angles to the direction of travel of the wave motion. They have **peaks** and **troughs**. Pull a rope tight, then move one end up and down, or side to side. A wave of energy travels along the rope. The rope itself doesn't travel. It is a **transverse wave**.

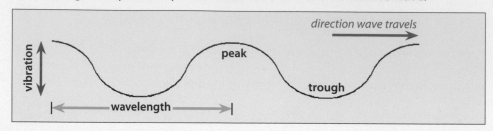

Longitudinal waves are waves in which the displacement of the particles is in line with, or parallel to, the direction of travel of the wave motion. Push and pull one end of a *Slinky* spring. Pushing causes **compression**. Pulling causes **rarefaction**. An energy wave travels along – the coils of the spring move back and forth. This is a **longitudinal wave**. The wave travels in the same direction as the vibration.

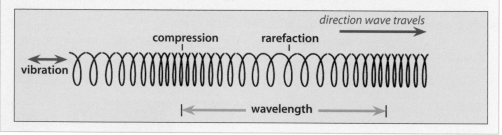

Wave properties

Amplitude (*a*) is the total distance between the crest of a wave and the centre line.

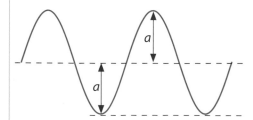

The **speed** of a wave (*v*) is the speed at which the vibrations in the wave move from one point to the next.

It's measured in metres per second (m/s, m s⁻¹). Typical speeds:

- The speed of sound in air is about 345 m s⁻¹
- The speed of light in a vacuum is 300 000 00 m s⁻¹ (3 x 10⁸ m s⁻¹)

Wavelength (λ) is the distance between one part of the wave and the next part which is at exactly the same stage of vibration. It's easiest if you think of it as the distance between one peak and the next.

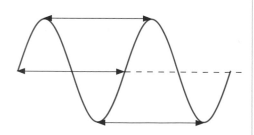

Frequency (*f*) is the number of complete waves passing a point each second. It's a *number per second* so it's measured in /s or s⁻¹: usually called hertz (Hz).

1 kilohertz = 1 kHz = 1000 Hz

1 megahertz = 1 MHz = 1 000 000 Hz

The wave equation

Question 1.1
These graphs show the same wave at time *t* (top graph) and time *t+1* ms (bottom graph).

(a) What is the speed of the wave?

(b) What is the wavelength?

The wavelength λ, wave velocity (speed) *v*, and frequency *f* are related by the wave equation:

$$v = f\lambda$$

(c) What is the frequency of the wave?

*(d) If this is a water wave and there is a float on the water at distance **d**, where will the float be after the wave has passed?*

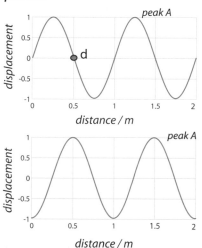

EM wave velocity

The speed of electromagnetic waves in a vacuum is always exactly the same value, which is very close to 3 x 10⁸ metres per second. This is often referred to as the speed of light, *c*.

The speed of the wave will depend on the medium in which is is travelling, but it can never be greater than *c*.

In air, electromagnetic waves travel at a speed very close to *c*.

Although all electromagnetic waves travel at the same speed, they can have different frequencies and wavelengths, resulting in different properties.

From the wave equation we can see that, as the frequency of the wave becomes larger, the wavelength will become smaller.

Electromagnetic v mechanical waves

Electromagnetic waves can transmit energy through a vacuum.

Mechanical waves cannot transmit energy through a vacuum.

Mechanical waves need a medium in which to transmit their energy:

- water waves – water
- sound waves – air
- slinky wave – the coils
- skipping rope – the rope
- mexican wave – spectators in a stadium

Electromagnetic (electrical and magnetic) waves produced in the Sun travel through outer space (a vacuum) to the Earth.

Question 1.2

(a) In space, distance is sometimes measured in light-years – the distance that light will travel in a year. How many kilometres are in a light year?

(b) The Sun is about 150 million km from Earth. How long will the light take to travel from the Sun to the Earth?

(c) Describe how the fans in a sports arena must move in order to produce a 'Mexican' wave. What kind of wave is this?

(d) An old TV programme, Star Trek, featured a spaceship called Enterprise. In the opening scene Enterprise is seen in space, moving across the screen making a whooshing sound.

Why would a young scientist disapprove of this?

Electromagnetic spectrum

There are many types of electromagnetic wave. When you place them in order of their frequencies, a spectrum is formed. **The greater the frequency of the wave the more energy it has and the more dangerous it is.**

All electromagnetic waves:

- travel at the same speed in a vacuum (3×10^8 metres per second, the speed of light) but can have wavelengths ranging from thousands of kilometres to a hundredth of a nanometre
- obey the wave equation (velocity = frequency x wavelength)
- undergo reflection, refraction, diffraction and can interfere with one another.

Properties of the radiation change depending on the wavelength and frequency. The range of all possible frequencies of electromagnetic radiation is called the **electromagnetic spectrum.**

Question 1.3

Many waves in the electromagnetic spectrum have wavelengths in a particular range. Assuming that the **maximum wavelength for microwaves is 10^{-3} m and for ultraviolet is 10^{-9} m**, what are the respective frequencies? Are these **maximum or minimum** frequencies?

The electromagnetic spectrum

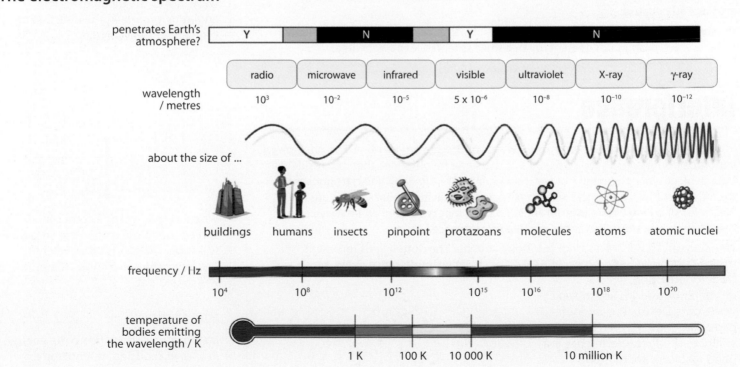

penetrates Earth's atmosphere?	Y		N		Y	N		
	radio	microwave	infrared	visible	ultraviolet	X-ray	γ-ray	
wavelength / metres	10^3	10^{-2}	10^{-5}	5×10^{-6}	10^{-8}	10^{-10}	10^{-12}	
about the size of ...	buildings	humans	insects	pinpoint	protazoans	molecules	atoms	atomic nuclei
frequency / Hz	10^4	10^8	10^{12}	10^{15}	10^{16}	10^{18}	10^{20}	
temperature of bodies emitting the wavelength / K		1 K	100 K	10 000 K		10 million K		

image © NASA

Sound waves

Sound waves are:

- longitudinal
- mechanical

They:

- have areas of high pressure (compression) and low pressure (rarefaction) alternately
- obey the law *velocity = frequency x wavelength*
- travel at approximately 345 m s^{-1} in air
- can be reflected, refracted, diffracted
- are subject to interference

Air pressure changes near the ear

... the peaks and troughs show how the air pressure varies:

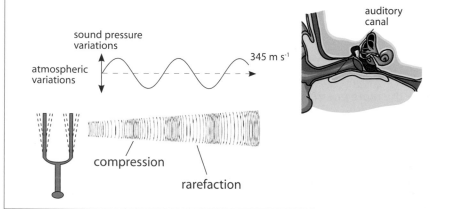

Attenuation

When waves decrease in amplitude, this is termed **attenuation**. Waves can be attenuated because:

- some of the energy they carry is absorbed by the medium they are travelling in
- as a wave propagates, the energy becomes spread over a larger area.

Interference

Interference occurs when two or more waves of the same type meet. The principle of superposition means that if two peaks of the same height meet, then the result will be a peak of twice the height of the individual peaks. Similarly, if two troughs meet, then the result will a trough twice as deep as the individual peaks. These are examples of **constructive interference**. If a peak meets a trough, then they can cancel each other out. This is **destructive interference**.

The diagram shows waves from two point sources. The dotted lines represent troughs. The solid lines represent peaks. Constructive interference peaks are shown by black dots. Constructive interference troughs are shown by white dots. Destructive interference points are shown by red dots. The ability to produce interference is a good test for wave motion.

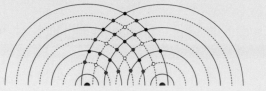

Direction

Usually waves travel in straight lines; the exception is when they encounter boundaries between different media. Rays can be reflected, refracted, diffracted or absorbed.

Reflection

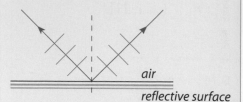

Waves will bounce off some surfaces. The velocity, wavelength and frequency will be unchanged.

Refraction

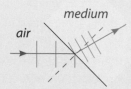

When a wave passes from one medium to another, its wavelength may change. For the frequency to remain the same the speed has changed. Unless the wave strikes the medium at right angles to its surface, the direction of propagation will change.

Diffraction

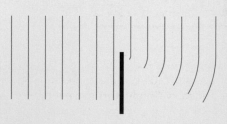

When a wave strikes a corner, it will spread round the corner. The amount it will spread depends on wavelength. The lower the wavelength, the more it will spread out.

Absorption

Materials will often absorb the energy in a wave, reducing its amplitude.

Electromagnetic waves: where do they come from, what do they do?

Electromagnetic radiation can be generated in many different ways.

Different methods produce radiation in different parts of the electromagnetic spectrum.

Thermal radiation

All objects with temperatures above absolute zero (0 Kelvin) give off electromagnetic radiation. The radiation has a **continuous spectrum**.

The intensity and frequency of the radiation increases with the temperature of the object.

Thermal radiation occurs naturally, for example sunlight, and is also created artificially, for example, by an incandescent light bulb.

Radioactive emissions

Some nuclei have structures which are unstable. In other words, the forces within the nuclei are not strong enough to keep the protons and neutrons in the same arrangement indefinitely.

When these nuclei change state in an attempt to become stable, they emit radiation in the form of particles or electromagnetic radiation – this is how γ-rays are produced. This can occur naturally (for example, from uranium found in the Earth), or it can be man made (for example, from bombarding stable nuclei with high energy neutrons to make unstable elements).

Uranium: a radioactive element found in the Earth

Interaction of electromagnetic waves with materials

It's not always easy to predict how electromagnetic waves will interact with materials.

As a very general rule, the longer the wavelength is, the more penetrating the wave will be. So radio waves can pass through walls, but visible light cannot. However, this isn't true in all cases. For example: some types of treated glass will let visible light through but block infrared, even though infrared has a longer wavelength than visible light.

In the X-ray and γ-ray region, everything changes. In this region, the higher the frequency, the more penetrating the radiation. The level of penetration will depend on the atomic number of the material the radiation is passing through – the higher the atomic number, the more radiation will be absorbed.

Conductors

Electromagnetic radiation in the lower frequency part of the spectrum (not above ultraviolet) will be reflected by conductors. Conductors can even have holes in them, and still reflect low frequency radiation, just as long as the holes are smaller than the wavelength of the radiation. For example, a microwave door will contain a metal mesh. The holes in the mesh will allow light to pass through the door, but the microwaves will be reflected and won't escape from the oven.

Question 2.1

(a) The door of a microwave oven contains a metal mesh to prevent the microwaves from escaping. If the holes of the mesh are 2 mm in diameter, what is the minimum wavelength of the radiation which the mesh will reflect?

(b) What is the maximum frequency?

Although you don't need to know everything on these two pages, it might help to recognise that medical physics plays only a part – albeit a very important part – in medical diagnosis and therapy.

Diagnosis

Medical practitioners diagnose causes of illness by looking for and carrying out basic tests for **symptoms**.

Symptoms are changes in normal body appearance or function. They indicate the cause of the illness.

Diagnosis may involve **biological** or **physical** factors.

Biological

Biological diagnosis includes:
- identification of organisms causing disease
- inspection of blood or other tissues for cell abnormalities
- chemical analysis
- genetic investigations.

Looking for cell abnormalities

Pathogens are not the only cause of disease. Other factors can harm tissues and their normal functioning.

Cancers, toxins, inherited defects and nutritional problems (excess as well as deficiencies) cause changes in the appearance of cells and tissues.

The process of taking a sample of body cells for analysis is called a biopsy.

Biopsy

- Punch biopsy utilises a special tool or a scalpel to remove cells from the surface of the skin or from organs exposed during surgery.
- Scraping utilises a special spatula such as for a cervical smear test.
- Endoscopic biopsy utilises small cutting tools
  - introduced to the body with a flexible endoscope
  - reaching tissue through an existing entrance such as throat or anus
  - avoiding surgery.
- Needle biopsy is used to sample blood and other tissue from organs beneath the skin, such as breast lumps, kidneys or bone marrow.

Physical

Physical diagnosis includes:
- measurements of the body's basic functions, such as temperature or blood pressure
- monitoring electrical activity, such as an electroencephalogram
- imaging, such as X-rays, thermography and scans.

Vital signs

Measurements of the body's basic functions or vital signs are useful for detecting or monitoring medical problems. Medical professionals usually monitor:
- body temperature
- pulse rate
- respiration rate
- blood pressure.

These measurements are quick and easy to take in a hospital or doctor's surgery, at home, at the site of a medical emergency or elsewhere.

Changes in vital signs indicate whether the patient is getting better or worse.

Norms

In a healthy person, body temperature and blood pressure vary, but within controlled limits. Homeostasis is automatic. It is the feedback mechanism keeping conditions inside the body within healthy limits. Norms are these boundaries within which the body systems work efficiently.

Medical imaging

Medical imaging is the process of examining parts of the patient's body which are not normally visible. These methods include:
- thermography
- X-rays and γ-cameras
- scans – CAT (computed axial tomography) and MRI (magnetic resonance imaging)
- endoscopy
- ultrasound.

They all require specialised equipment and skilled operators.

The techniques are generally non- or minimally-invasive.

Electrical activity

- in the brain is traced on an electroencephalogram
- traced by an electrocardiograph indicates the performance of the heart.

Therapeutic techniques

Physical techniques

Therapeutic drugs may be used in many cases of chemical imbalance in the body or to combat invading organisms.

Many other causes of ill health can't be treated by drug therapy or by drugs alone. Physical techniques which will alleviate or cure them include:

- surgery
- replacement surgery
- radiotherapy
- laser therapy
- physiotherapy, osteopathy and chiropractics
- acupuncture and other alternative therapies
- preventive therapies
- vaccination
- organ transplants
- blood and plasma transfusion.

Radiotherapy

Radiotherapy uses radiation, such as X-rays or γ-rays, for the treatment of localised cancers and, occasionally, other diseases. It's often used following surgery to destroy any remaining cancer cells. Measured doses of radiation are used to destroy tumour cells with the minimum damage to the surrounding tissues.

Vaccination

Vaccinations effectively teach the body how to make antibodies to destroy disease-causing organisms (pathogens).

Organ transplants

Organs removed from donors replace damaged or failing organs, such as a kidney.

Surgery

Modern surgical techniques can be used to remove diseased tissue and repair or replace damaged or malfunctioning structures. Life threatening or painful conditions, from cancerous tumours and deep seated abscesses to damaged knee cartilages, can be treated. Failed joints or eye lenses can be replaced. In cosmetic surgery, appearances may be improved.

Replacement surgery

Joint replacement surgery is highly effective for removing joint pain, correcting deformity and restoring movement, for example in advanced arthritis.

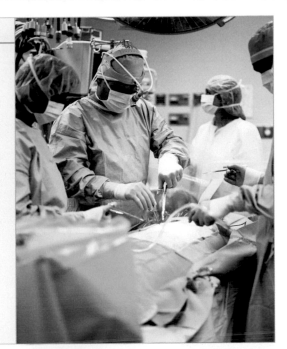

Physiotherapy, osteopathy and chiropractics

These three offer different approaches to the treatment of the human movement systems – muscles, joints and skeleton. As well as manipulation and exercise, therapies include ultrasound.

Physical problems may be caused by illness, accident or ageing.

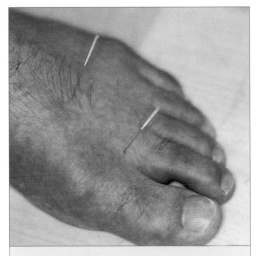

Acupuncture

Acupuncture is a branch of traditional Chinese medicine, practised for thousands of years. It's a form of alternative medicine, used to treat pain. Ultra-fine metal needles are inserted at carefully selected points on the skin.

Laser therapy

Lasers deliver highly accurate, high energy beams. They are used for a variety of microsurgical techniques, including the removal of birthmarks and the treatment of eye defects. In short sight, the lens system of the eye is too powerful. Laser surgery slightly flattens the centre of the cornea.

Blood transfusions

Blood transfusions are often life saving, e.g. if there has been massive blood loss in an accident or surgery, or in severe anaemia such as in sickle cell disease.

Preventive therapies

A great many techniques can prevent or slow down the onset of disease, for example, regular exercise.

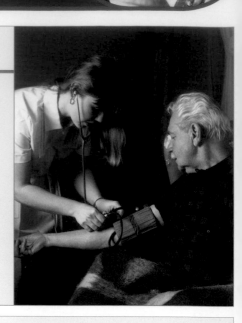

Physiological measurements

Systems in the human body are complex and should be assessed and monitored by measuring several parameters simultaneously rather than on their own.

Physiology is the study of the functions of living matter and how an organism performs (in other words, how it adapts to changes in its internal and external environment).

Some physiological measurements used to assess the health and well being of patients:

- body temperature – commonly using thermometers
- blood pressure – invasive and non-invasive methods including the sphygmomanometer
- brain activity – electroencephalogram (EEG)
- heart activity – electrocardiogram (ECG)

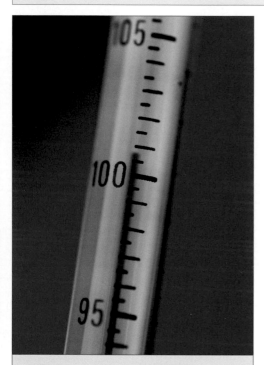

standard liquid-in-glass thermometer

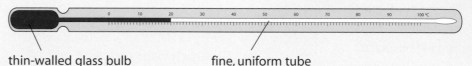

thin-walled glass bulb   fine, uniform tube

clinical thermometer

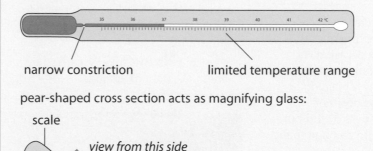

narrow constriction   limited temperature range

pear-shaped cross section acts as magnifying glass:

scale

view from this side

Thermometers

There are different types of thermometer.

Any property of a material which changes with temperature can be used to indicate or measure temperature.

For example:

- the expansion of liquids in **liquid-in-glass** thermometers
- the change in resistance of a semiconductor material with temperature in a **thermistor** thermometer
- change in colour of a thermochromic liquid crystal sheet.

Liquid-in-glass thermometers

Mercury-in-glass and alcohol-in-glass thermometers use the cubical expansion of a liquid to measure temperature. Design details:

- the liquid is contained in a thin-walled glass bulb
- the amount of liquid should be small
- the tube is uniform, to give even expansion
- the tube is fine.

Clinical thermometer extra features:

- A narrow constriction in the tube just above the bulb allows the expanding liquid to force its way past. When the liquid in the bulb contracts, the liquid in the tube is trapped. Thus the temperature can be read after the thermometer has been removed from the patient.
- A limited range of temperatures from 35 to 42 ° Celsius. A fine tube gives 1/5 ° or 1/10 ° sensitivity
- The pear-shaped cross section acts as a magnifying glass making it easier to read.

Question 3.1

Explain why:

(a) *the glass wall of a thermometer bulb should be thin*

(b) *the volume of liquid in a thermometer should be small*

(c) *the tube should be uniform*

(d) *the tube is fine*

(e) *medical professionals 'shake' clinical thermometers after taking a patient's temperature.*

Thermistor thermometers

Resistance in a resistor varies with temperature. A thermistor is a *very* temperature-sensitive resistance made from a semiconductor.

When thermal energy is transferred to the thermistor, this transforms into kinetic energy. This energy releases any loosely held electrons. The mobile electrons alter the material – it changes from being an insulator to a conductor. With increasing temperature, yet more electrons are freed and the conducting ability substantially increases.

In a digital thermometer, the change in the thermistor's resistance is calibrated against temperature. The temperature is then relayed to a liquid crystal-based display.

Ear thermometers are an example of themistor thermometers.

liquid-in-glass v thermistor

type of thermometer	advantages	disadvantages
liquid-in-glass	convenient	fragile
	portable	mercury, if used, is toxic
		limited range
	cheap	cannot record temperatures automatically or electronically
thermistor	easy to read	batteries need replacing
	temperature reading can be recorded automatically and electronically	more expensive
	more robust	

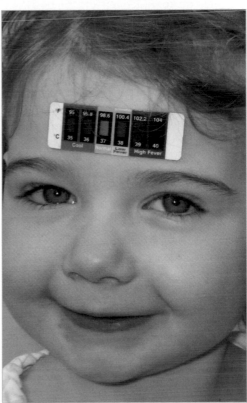

This type of forehead thermometer uses thermochromic liquid crystals. It is not as accurate as liquid-in-glass or thermistor thermometers.

Using body temperature as an indicator of health

What is body temperature?

Vital signs are measurements of the body's most basic functions. One of the main vital signs routinely monitored by medical professionals is body temperature.

The *normal* body temperature of a person varies depending on gender, recent activity, food and fluid consumption, time of day and, in women, the stage of the menstrual cycle. Normal body temperature can range from 36.5 °C to 37.2 °C.

Normal **temperature, measured orally, is considered to be 36.8 °C.**

A person's body temperature can be taken in any of the following ways:

*   Orally – in the mouth (liquid-in-glass or digital thermometer)
*   Rectally – temperature taken this way tends to be slightly **higher** than when taken orally (liquid-in-glass or digital thermometer)
*   Axillary – temperature taken under the armpit tends to be slightly **lower** than when taken orally (liquid-in-glass or digital thermometer)
*   Tympanic – requires a special thermometer to measure the temperature of the ear drum, which reflects the body's core temperature

All temperatures referred to in this section are temperatures taken in the mouth

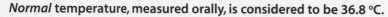
Normal body temperature is considered to be 36.8 °C.

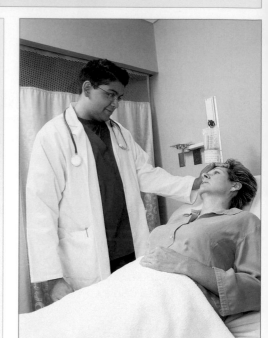

Hypothermia

Hypothermia – body temperature **decreases** to 32 °C or lower.

Symptoms

Hypothermia develops gradually.

35 to 36 °C

*   feeling cold, shivering

34 °C or lower

*   People shiver uncontrollably, become clumsy, drowsy, confused, pale, slurred speech, skin feels cold. As their core body temperature decreases, shivering stops and people become unconscious.

At low body temperature

*   brain, nervous systems and heart rate slow
*   heart rhythm may become irregular
*   blood pressure falls
*   digestion slows – peristalsis fails
*   kidneys make less urine

Below 30 °C

*   organs stop working
*   death is likely

Fever

Fever occurs when body temperature is higher than normal for that individual. It is a sign that there is an abnormal process going on within the body.

Generally, a body temperature above 37.2 °C indicates fever.

Death

Cold

25 °C or less.

Death usually occurs due to irregular heart beat or respiratory arrest.

Some patients have been known to survive with body temperatures as low as 14.2 °C

Hot

43 °C or above.

Normally death, or there may be serious brain damage, continuous convulsions and shock. Cardio-respiratory collapse will occur. Death becomes more certain as the temperature exceeds 43 °C.

Hyperthermia

Hyperthermia – body temperature **increases** to 38 °C or higher in the absence of infection. Hyperthermia is the clinical name for *heat exhaustion* and *heat stroke*.

Symptoms

As the temperature rises, sweating and thirst are followed by

- headache
- nausea
- muscle cramps
- weakness
- dizziness
- fainting as blood pressure drops
- confusion, aggression

Above 40 °C

- blindness
- unconsciousness
- death is likely

All temperatures referred to in the sections *Hypothermia, Fever, Hyperthermia* and *Death* are temperatures taken in the mouth.

Question 4.1

Which is likely to give the most reliable temperature measurement, mouth or rectum? Give reasons why.

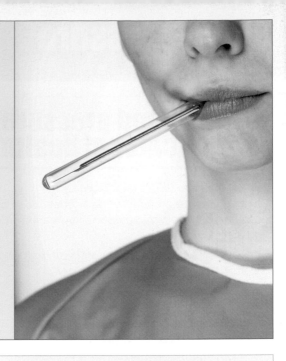

Question 4.2

Hyperthermia progresses to a point where the skin is hot. This is considered to be an extreme medical emergency. Why can the body no longer cool itself? What might be a consequence of this?

Question 4.3

Across:

4 The clinical name for heat exhaustion and heat stroke.

7 In hypothermia the kidneys make less of this.

8 (and 6 down) The temperature taken here is close to body core temperature.

9 Temperature which is lower than that taken orally (in the mouth).

Down:

1 The body produces this in order to cool down.

2 This may cause the heartbeat to slow down and become irregular.

3 Likely result of a body temperature over 43 °C.

5 What describes body condition when its temperature rises above 37.2 °C.

6 see 8 across.

Blood pressure

Using blood pressure as an indicator of health

Blood pressure (BP) is generated by the force of the heart pumping blood into the arteries. It can be measured using a manual sphygmomanometer or an electronic monitor.

In both, a cuff is inflated to a pressure high enough to stop the flow of blood in the artery.

- The pressure is reduced slowly until an intermittent blood flow is detected. This is the **systolic blood pressure**.
- The pressure is reduced further until a constant blood flow is detected. This is the **diastolic blood pressure**.

The unit of measurement is kilopascal (kPa), though many practitioners still use millimetres of mercury (mm Hg).

Normal blood pressure

A vital sign routinely monitored by medical professionals is blood pressure.

Normal blood pressure is within a range. The range varies with age, fitness and health. Readings are comparative with a person's normal value. You must know normal blood pressures for healthy young adults:

- male 125/80 mm Hg
- female 123/80 mm Hg

Other typical values:

- at birth 80/50 mmHg
- 20 year-old pregnant female 90/80 mm Hg
- 40 year-old female 133/85 mm Hg
- elderly man 160/85 mm Hg

Manual non-invasive blood pressure measurement

A sphygmomanometer has a cuff that is inflated around a patient's arm until the blood flow stops. The pressure is measured using a mercury or mechanical manometer. Air to inflate the cuff is supplied through a bulb, with a non-return valve in the cuff. Pressure is released through a screw valve.

The cuff is wrapped around the upper left arm, at about the same height as the heart, with the centre of the inflatable part over the brachial artery. The cuff is inflated until the blood flow in the artery ceases. The pressure is then slowly released while the medical professional listens for sounds in the artery, using a stethoscope.

When blood flow in the artery first starts again, a sound can be heard: the systolic blood pressure. As pressure in the cuff is further released, the sound dies away: the diastolic blood pressure.

In the cardiac cycle:

- systolic pressure gives the peak pressure
- diastolic pressure gives the resting pressure.

Electronic sphygmomanometers will inflate and deflate the cuff automatically. They give a digital readout of systolic pressure, diastolic pressure and pulse rate.

> **Question 5.1**
> *What is meant by invasive and non-invasive techniques?*

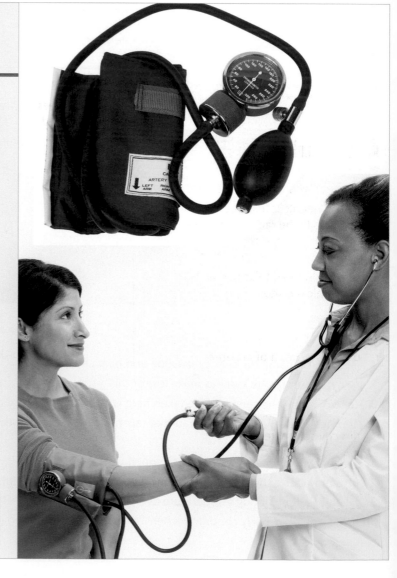

Sounds in the brachial artery

Phase 1

Cuff is inflated to beyond the **systolic** pressure, artery is completely blocked, no sounds. As pressure is released there is a sharp tapping sound. The blood flow is **turbulent**.

Phase 4

Sound abruptly muffled, blood flow almost returned to normal, flow becomes **laminar**. This is at **diastolic** pressure.

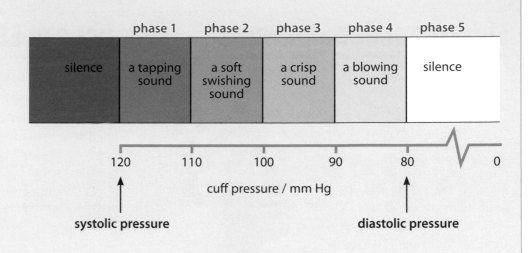

Question 5.2

(a) Why must the cuff be at roughly the same height as the heart?

(b) What happens in the period of silence that a medical professional hears through their stethoscope?

(c) What exactly is happening during the periods of tapping, swishing and blowing that a medical professional hears through their stethoscope, in between the systolic and diastolic silence zones?

Invasive arterial blood pressure measurement

Direct measurement of arterial pressure.

A cannula needle is inserted into an artery (usually the radial or brachial artery in the arm, the femoral artery in the leg or the dorsalis pedis in the foot.

A sterile, fluid-filled tube connects to an electronic monitor.

Advantages

- constant monitoring
- displays a graph of *pressure* against *time*.

Disadvantages

- needs close supervision
- directly connected to artery: accidental disconnection results in serious bleeding

Uses

- for critically ill patients with rapid variation in blood pressure
- during operations.

Question 5.3

Our blood pressure can and will vary. Suppose that, in the morning just before you get out of bed, your systolic/diastolic blood pressure is 104/78 mm Hg.

Select systolic/diastolic blood pressures from this list to match the statements:

- 130/70
- 149/79
- 128/74
- 164/68

(a)	You have some breakfast and a large cup of coffee to try to wake yourself up.	
(b)	You go to the library, log onto the internet, check a few emails, phone your mate to check they've done their coursework, and have another coffee.	
(c)	You go to your first class and the teacher says something really annoying.	
(d)	End of lesson, you and your friends let of steam by moaning about the teacher, you go for a wander and decide: "life ain't so bad!"	

Brain and heart activity

Electroencephalograms

Electroencephalograms (EEG) can show whether sections of the brain are functioning correctly.

The brain produces electrical signals. These are picked up through electrodes attached to the scalp. The signals, in the form of waves, are recorded and plotted graphically.

There are four types of wave: **delta**, **theta**, **alpha** and **beta** for typical shapes of **spontaneous brain potentials**.

image: corbis

Uses of EEGs

The EEG is a painless test.
An EEG can be used to:

- diagnose epilepsy and identify type of seizures
- diagnose head injuries, brain haemorrhage, spinal cord or nervous system problems
- check for problems with loss of consciousness or dementia
- investigate brain tumours
- evaluate recovery after a change in consciousness
- find out if a person who is in a persistent coma is brain dead
- study sleep disorders
- check brain activity during brain surgery

EEG brainwave sample	brainwave frequency	state of consciousness
(waveform)	Delta 0.5 – 4 Hz	deep sleep; highest in amplitude;
(waveform)	Theta 4 - 8 Hz	deeply relaxed; slow activity; bursts of creative ideas
(waveform)	Alpha 8 - 12 Hz	relaxed; right-brain thinking activity – subconscious mind
(waveform)	Beta 12 - 30 Hz	awake and alert; fast activity; left-brain thinking activity – conscious mind

Electrocardiograms

Electrocardiograms are also called ECG or EKG. It is a record of the electrical activity of the heart:

- how fast it's beating
- rhythm
- strength
- timing.

Heart problems can be located with an electrocardiogram.

Electrical signals travel from the sino-atrial node in the right atrium to the lower part of the heart. This causes the muscle to contract – a heartbeat. The atria contract to fill the ventricles and then the ventricles contract to pump blood out to the rest of the body.

Normally, 12 probes are placed on the body to record activity (a12-lead ECG). Six- and two-lead ECGs are also sometimes made.

Normal sinus rhythm

Normal sinus rhythm is the rhythm of a healthy normal heart. The sinus rhythm is normal if its frequency is between 60 and 100 beats per minute. Often there's a degree of arrhythmia (in other words, some variation of the wave shape).

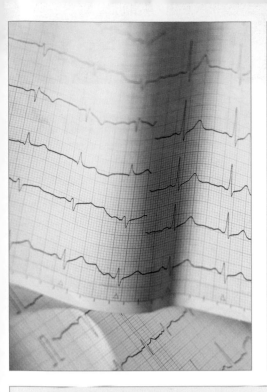

PQRST

ECGs are typically done in a GP's surgery or hospital. The results are recorded as a graph which shows if the patient has a normal heart rhythm.

Scientists label the different points of the ECG as **P, Q, R, S** and **T**:

- Atrial systole **P** wave
- Ventricular systole **QRS** complex
- Ventricular diastole **ST** wave

Question 6.1

A normal ECG trace is shown, right.

Label the points of the graph that represent PQRST.

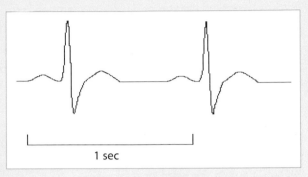

1 sec

Question 6.2

(a) In order for a medical professional to determine the normal sinus rhythms of a patient, the patient needs to be relaxed and still. Why is this necessary while an ECG trace is being taken?

(b) What medical conditions might a slow heart be a symptom of? How could you discriminate between the conditions?

Irregular heartbeats

Arrhythmia or irregular heart rhythm can cause the heart to beat too slowly (**bradycardia**) or too fast (**sinus tachycardia**). The graphs, below, show four patients' ECG traces. *Question 6.3: Join the diagnoses and symptoms to their trace ...*

diagnosis and symptoms	trace
Sinus tachycardia: Sinus rhythm is faster than 100 beats per minute. Rhythm is similar to normal but RR interval is shorter. **Symptoms:** A normal response to exercise, stress or anger. Can also indicate blood flow is restricted or isn't circulating properly (sometimes after heart attack).	A
Bradycardia: Heart rate is slower than 60 beats per minute. Rhythm is similar to normal but RR interval is longer. **Symptoms:** Extreme tiredness, dizziness, fainting and shortness of breath, difficult or painful breathing.	B
Sinus arrhythmia: Disturbances in the heart's regular rhythm. RR and PP intervals are not regularly spaced. **Symptoms:** Can be life-threatening causing cardiac arrest and sudden death. Other cases are milder such as being aware the heart is beating differently or palpitating. Some are quite benign and normal.	C
Ventricular fibrillation: Parts of the ventricles depolarise repeatedly in an erratic uncoordinated way. **Symptoms:** Little or no blood being pumped, so the patient will lose consciousness, go into cardiac arrest and die without resuscitation.	D

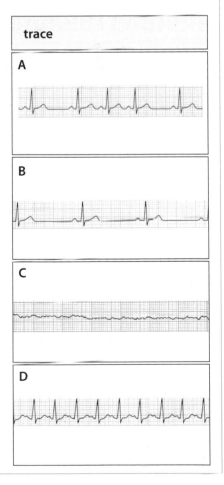

Thermography

Thermography

Temperature on the surface of a body can be a good indicator of what might be going on inside. Skin temperature:

- rises with increased blood flow and metabolic rate
- lowers where the blood flow is restricted.

Such areas can signify abnormality such as tumour, disease or injury.

Thermography utilises infrared cameras to photograph the patient's body. The image on the screen will show the areas of tissue with raised temperatures.

It is non-invasive.

This photo shows a medical professional aiming a thermography camera at a patient's hands. The patient's fingers are cold which may indicate poor blood circulation.

d. ermakoff/eurelios/science photo library

Thermal radiation

All solids, liquids and dense gas above 0 Kelvin (absolute zero) give off some electromagnetic radiation.

The intensity and frequency of the radiation will depend on the temperature of the object and on how good the object is at emitting the radiation.

This radiation is known as **hot-body radiation**, or **thermal radiation**, even though the objects emitting it may not be at a temperature we would describe as *hot*.

Infrared and thermal images

Near-infrared photography detects high frequency / short wavelength infrared – close to the visible spectrum.

Thermal cameras detect infrared radiation with a longer wavelength / lower frequency – images look very different from those made by a conventional camera as the intensity depends mainly on the thermal radiation being emitted by an object.

Active infrared imaging – the scene is illuminated by infrared radiation (the equivalent of using a flash in conventional photography).

Heat and infrared

Temperature is a measure of how much kinetic energy molecules have.

At 0 Kelvin, molecules are assumed to have no kinetic energy. They are, therefore, completely still.

The energy in infrared radiation is easily absorbed by molecules, causing them to vibrate which increases their temperature.

Warm and hot objects will emit thermal radiation in the infrared part of the electromagnetic spectrum, so infrared radiation can transfer heat from one object to another.

This method of heat transfer is sometimes called radiated heat.

When heat is transferred in this way, the energy changes from kinetic energy to infrared energy then back to kinetic energy.

Humans are normally able to maintain a constant internal temperature, regardless of the external environment. Any heat disperses through the skin. The skin radiates high intensity infrared in the surrounding environment.

The hotter an object - the greater is the energy carried away by infrared radiation.

An object heated until it glows emits visible radiation and infrared radiation.

Thermal radiation covers visible and infrared radiation.

False colour in thermal imaging

False colour is often used in thermal imaging. Real colour allows us to distinguish between light of different frequencies.

In thermal imaging, false colour can allow us to distinguish between objects of different temperatures. Different colours are assigned to different temperatures.

Question 7.1

What sort of radiation is given off by

(a) a human hand

(b) a red hot poker?

Question 7.2

Before a patient receives a thermograph they spend time in a cooled room. Explain why.

How a thermal camera works

A thermal camera works in a similar way to a normal digital camera. The infrared image is focused by a lens onto an array of sensors. These sensors detect the intensity of the radiation and turn it into electrical signals. These signals are then processed to produce an image that can be saved or displayed.

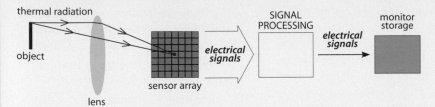

Thermal cameras – like all objects – give off some thermal radiation. This produces unwanted signals and decreases the sensitivity of the camera. To prevent this, thermal cameras are **cryogencially-cooled**. This makes them more expensive and less robust.

Sensors

Thermal cameras rely on sensors which can detect the intensity of infrared radiation.

Usually a sensor array is used. The sensors are only sensitive to radiation in a limited frequency band. The electrical signal produced will depend on the intensity of the radiation landing on the sensor.

The more sensors that are used, the sharper the resulting image will be.

Question 7.4

In the graph, the thermal radiation intensity is plotted against wavelength for bodies at 300 K, 310 K and 373K.

Use the graph to explain why infrared radiation is a good choice for looking at humans.

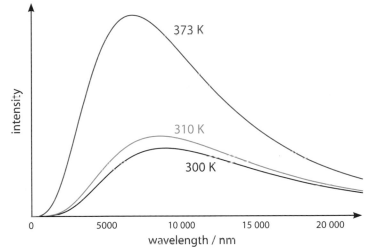

Question 7.3

Look at the thermograph of a car. Which colour shows:

(a) the warmest temperature

(b) the coolest temperature?

The pros and cons of thermography

PROS
• no risk as there is no harmful radiation
• early detection of problems
• coverage of a whole area
• precise location of problem area prepares for other precision tests: ultrasound, mammogram, MRI
• no pain, pressure or touching by equipment/technician

CONS
• cameras are expensive and easily damaged
• image interpretation requires experienced professionals
• surfaces only
• training is time consuming
• focusing difficulty with infrared rays
• image quality lacks sharpness, resolution and detail

Question 7.5

Across:

2 An area of decreased temperature might show a restriction in the flow of this.

4 Bodies with a temperature above absolute zero emit this radiation.

5 Thermography is popular with patients because the procedure involves no _____.

6 One advantage of thermography is the lack of _____.

7 Thermographs detect temperatures on human _____.

8 The hotter an object, the more _____ given off per second.

Down:

1 Makes thermographs a useful method of investigating possible illness.

3 It's expensive to buy a high _____ thermal camera.

Radiation

Radiation and isotopes

Ionising radiation can be used to *treat* some cancers by destroying cancer cells. Radioactive substances can also be used to help medical professionals monitor what is going on in some parts of the body. This involves ionising radiation being put into the body and using machines to detect the radioactivity. However, ionising radiation *causes* some cancers – using radioactivity for treatment must be carefully controlled.

Isotopes of an element have the same number of protons, but a different number of neutrons. For example, there are three carbon isotopes:

carbon-12   each atoms has 6 protons and 6 neutrons

carbon-13   each atoms has 6 protons and 7 neutrons

carbon-14   each atoms has 6 protons and 8 neutrons

Changing the number of protons would give a different element.

The mass number of an atom is the sum of the protons and neutrons in its nucleus (electrons have negligible mass). An element's relative atomic mass is the weighted average of the mass numbers of its isotopes in a naturally occurring sample of the element.

Isotopes exhibit the same chemical properties as each other.

Question 8.1

The relative atomic mass of chlorine is 35.5. Chlorine (atomic number 17) has two isotopes: chlorine-35 (mass number 35) and chlorine-37 (mass number 37). Calculate the ratio of these two isotopes in chlorine.

Radioactivity

If an isotope has an unstable nucleus, the nucleus will decay into a stable state. When this happens, it emits radiation:

- α (alpha) particles *(intensely ionising; +ve charge)*
- β (beta) particles *(less ionising; -ve charge)*
- γ (gamma) rays *(barely ionising; very short length EM radiation)*

The emission of α and β particles results in a change to the element.

α decay – the particle emitted is a helium nucleus (2p, 2n): the element changes.

β decay – the electrons in the nucleus change: a proton becomes a neutron: the element changes.

γ rays do not involve a change in the number of protons or neutrons.

Radiation units and organ sensitivity

The becquerel (Bq) is a unit used to measure radioactivity. A quantity of radioactive material with radioactivity of one becquerel has one unstable nucleus changing and emitting radiation every second.

When ionising radiation interacts with biological tissue, it deposits energy there. The amount of energy deposited per unit mass of tissue is called the absorbed dose: the unit of this dose is called the gray (Gy).

1 Gy is 1 joule deposited per kilogram of material. The unit that measures the likelihood of harm is called the sievert (Sv). This is known as the **dose equivalent**.

Equal exposures to different types of radiation do not necessarily produce equal biological effects. It depends on the weighting factor of the radiation source.

dose equivalent (Sv) = absorbed dose (Gy) x weighting factor

Example:

A medical professional is subjected to 0.2 mGy of alpha radiation in one year. What is the dose equivalent?

Using the equation:

dose equivalent (Sv) = absorbed dose (Gy) x weighting factor = 0.2 x 10 = **2 mSv**

Regardless of the type of radiation, one sievert of radiation produces the same biological effect.

Sensitivity of organs to radiation (organ affinity)

Various human tissues and organs have different affinities (organ affinity) to the same amount of radiation. The annual radiation exposure limit of 20 mSv for radiation workers is based on the whole body dose equivalent amount. Tissue weighting factors depend on the type of tissue or organ.

ionising radiation source	weighting factor (WR)
γ-rays	1
X-rays	1
beta particles	1
alpha particles	10
slow neutrons	5
fast neutrons	10

tissue or organ	tissue weighting factor
bone surface	0.01
colon	0.12
breast	0.05
liver	0.05
skin	0.01
gonads	0.20
lung	0.12

Question 8.2

(a) Why do alpha particles have such a high weighting factor?

(b) In one year a doctor is subjected to 50 mGy of X-rays and 0.4 mGy of alpha radiation. What's the total dose equivalent?

(c) (i) Which tissue or organ has the highest sensitivity towards ionising radiation?

(ii) What effect might over-exposure have?

(d) Why are effective dose values different?

Background radiation

We're exposed to radiation from natural sources all the time. This background radiation comes from naturally occurring radioactive materials and cosmic radiation from outer space. It varies with geographical location and the geology under your feet. In Cornwall, residents can receive over 0.3 mSv per year, because of its geology.

Ionising radiation

Energy from high frequency electromagnetic radiation can be absorbed by an atom's electrons. Sometimes this gives an electron enough energy to escape from the atom completely. The radiation is therefore **ionising radiation**. This may result in molecular bonds being broken, and the rearrangement or breaking up of molecules. In living organisms, ionising radiation can lead to cell damage, which can lead to the death or mutation of the cell.

In the electromagnetic spectrum, only radiation with frequencies in the ultraviolet range and above are ionising. The higher the frequency of the radiation, the more energy an individual electron will receive, and the more likely ionisation becomes.

The DNA of the cell contains the information needed for the cell to maintain itself and reproduce. If this is damaged, then the cell may die or be unable to reproduce properly. If it does reproduce, it may pass the damaged instructions on to the new cells. Cells have the ability to repair their own DNA so, unless the level of radiation is very high, the cells will often be able to recover – but there is the possibility of long-term damage. Cells which reproduce quickly may not have time to repair themselves, and are therefore more likely to be affected by radiation.

Question 8.3

The diagram shows the three types of radiation penetrating various materials. Add labels to show which is alpha (α) particles, beta (β) particles and gamma (γ) rays.

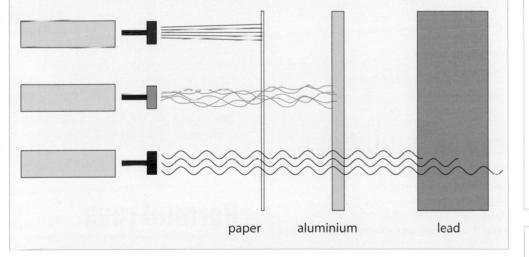

paper   aluminium   lead

Question 8.4

(a) Sources of which ionising radiation would be the safest to ingest? Why?

(b) Iridium-192 is a chemical used in medical physics.

(i) What does the number 192 represent?

(ii) If an atom of iridium-192 emits an alpha particle, what happens to the 192?

Question 8.5

The half-life of an isotope of nitrogen is 7.3 s. What does this mean? A sample of this type of nitrogen is observed for 29.2 s. Calculate the fraction of the original radioactive isotope remaining after this time.

Radioactive decay

Radioactive decay is random. If you could see an individual nucleus within a sample of a radioactive material, it might decay within one second, two hours, 76 days or millions of years. However, since there are billions of nuclei within the sample, the decay pattern is random.

A radioactive isotope decays uniquely with its own half-life.

A half-life of a sample of radioactive substance is the time taken for half the original number of unstable atoms to decay.

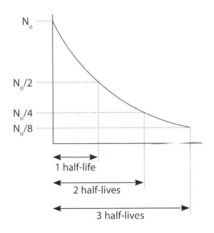

Suppose a radioactive isotope X has N_o atoms initially present.

- After one half-life $0.5\ N_o$ atoms of X have disintegrated and $0.5\ N_o$ atoms of X remain.

- After two half-lives from the start $0.25\ N_o$ atoms of X remain and $0.75\ No$ atoms of X have disintegrated.

- After three half-lives, $0.125\ N_o$ atoms remain etc.

- Decay is exponential.

Question 8.6

What is the half-life of this source?

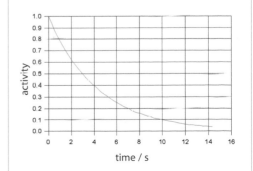

Stochastic and non-stochastic

When radiation dose varies, harm to tissues varies predictably or unpredictably.

- **Stochastic effects**, such as cancer, occur randomly. They become more likely with increased dose but do not vary in severity.
- **Non-stochastic (deterministic) effects**, such as hair loss, vary in severity according to the dosage above a threshold level.

Examples of radiation effects

Stochastic

Cancers or inherited diseases can be caused by radiation damage to DNA. Such damage is unpredictable. It may occur in:

- non-functional DNA or in cells which don't divide and have no detectable effect
- dividing cells in body tissues which become cancerous and divide out of control (non-transmissible somatic effects)
- cells in the reproductive organs which form sperm or egg cells and cause inherited disorders in children (transmissible hereditary effects).

Note: Harm either occurs in full or not at all. There is no threshold, but the risk of inducing cancer or hereditary disorder increases with the radiation dose.

Non-stochastic

Diarrhoea induced by radiation varies according to the dose:

- insufficient cells are damaged to have any effect up to a threshold dose
- above the threshold enough of the small intestine lining is affected to cause symptoms
- the amount of tissue damage and the severity of the diarrhoea increases directly with the radiation dose once the threshold has been passed.

Question 9.1

Sort these into deterministic and stochastic effects.

(a) cataracts   (b) leukaemia   (c) tumours   (d) sun burn

Radiographers and radiologists

Radiographers are healthcare professionals who work with X-rays and γ-rays. There are two types of radiographers. Diagnostic radiographers use medical imaging techniques to produce images for the diagnosis of injury or disease. Therapeutic radiographers plan and deliver radiotherapy for the treatment of cancer.

Radiologists are doctors who specialise in interpreting X-rays and other types of scans.

Levels of risk from X-ray examinations

Estimate of risks associated with different types of X-ray examination:

type of examination	equivalent period of background radiation	lifetime additional risk of cancer per examination
chest, teeth, arms and legs, hands and feet	a few days	negligible risk (less than 1 in 1 000 000)
skull, head, neck	a few weeks	minimal risk (1 in 1 000 000 to 1 in 100 000)
breast (mammography), spine, hip, abdomen, pelvis, CAT scan of head	a few months to a year	very low risk (1 in 100 000 to 1 in 10 000)
kidneys and bladder, stomach – barium meal, colon – barium enema, CAT scan of chest, CAT scan of abdomen	a few years	low risk (1 in 10 000 to 1 in 1000)

Harmful rays

Although X-rays and γ-rays are very useful for diagnosing and treating medical conditions, they are hazardous in ways that other parts of the electromagnetic spectrum are not. A balance needs to be struck between the benefits to the patients and the risks associated with exposure to ionising radiation.

In order to protect patients and staff, it is necessary to minimise the dose they receive and monitor the level of exposure.

Minimising exposure

Exposure should not exceed recommended limits, and all exposures should be kept As Low As Reasonably Achievable (ALARA).

Exposure can be reduced by:

- reducing exposure time
- increasing distance from the source – X-rays and γ-rays follow the inverse square law
- decreasing the strength or size of the source
- shielding
- wearing lead aprons
- standing behind screens
- leaving the room.

Question 9.2

If the half-value thickness of lead is 1 cm, what thickness is needed to reduce the radiation intensity to one eighth of its original value?

Shielding

Lead is often used for shielding because it's good at absorbing radiation.

Glass containing lead is also used for shielding. This allows staff to safely observe procedures such as CAT scans. The plaster on the walls of rooms where ionising radiation is used may contain barium sulfate to absorb the radiation. The walls may be very thick, with the concrete in them to provide shielding.

The amount of radiation a material absorbs will depend on its thickness. The thickness of a material needed to reduce the intensity of radiation to half its initial value is called the **half-value thickness**. The half-value thickness will depend on the frequency of the radiation.

For γ-rays, the half-value thickness of concrete is about four times that of lead.

Hospital employee working behind a glass wall during a CAT scan

public domain image

Safety measures for staff

- Film badges:

  Film badges are badges containing film which is sensitive to ionising radiation. They are worn by staff working with X-rays and γ-rays and can provide a permanent record of the radiation the staff member was exposed to.

  Film badges are a type of **dosimeter**. A dosimeter is a device for measuring the amount of radiation the wearer has been exposed to.

- Working in controlled areas:

  A controlled area is a place with restricted access, where anyone entering must follow special procedures designed to limit exposure.

- Hazard signs/lights to keep out other people.
- Equipment checked regularly.
- Codes of conduct.

Safety measures for internal radiotherapy

With internal radiotherapy, a radioactive substance is placed within the patient's body. The patient will be radioactive and may require special precautions.

- Separation from patients who are not receiving similar treatment.
- Lead screens on either side of the bed.
- Visitors only allowed to stay for short periods.
- No children under 16 or pregnant women allowed to visit.
- Staff will only stay in the room for a short length of time.
- Staff may use a Geiger counter to monitor levels of radiation.
- Staff and visitors will keep at a safe distance from patient.

Diagnosis

A radioisotope used for diagnosis must emit γ-rays of sufficient energy to escape from the body and it must have a half-life short enough for it to decay away soon after imaging is complete.

Radiotherapy

Ionising radiation is more likely to kill cancer cells than healthy cells. It can therefore be used to treat cancer. This is called **radiotherapy**. The radiation can either be given from outside the body (**external radiotherapy**) or from inside the body (**internal radiotherapy**).

Radiotherapy treatment can be used to:

- cure cancer
- alleviate the effects of cancer
- shrink a tumour prior to surgery
- kill any remaining cancer cells after surgery
- total body irradiation (given to people having bone marrow transplants to kill existing bone marrow cells).

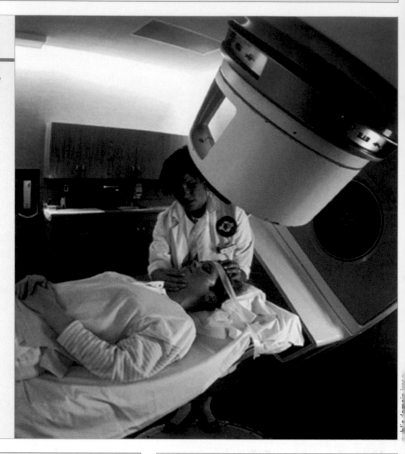

External radiotherapy

In external radiotherapy, a source of ionising radiation – either an X-ray tube or a radioactive source of γ-rays – is directed at the tumour. The treatment is repeated at intervals designed to give healthy tissue a chance to recover. The individual treatments are called fractions. The positioning and shape of the radiation is carefully planned so that the tumour has as much exposure as possible, and the healthy tissue as little as possible.

Question 10.1

(a) Why might rays be directed at a tumour from several different angles?

(b) Why might small tattoos be made on the skin before radiotherapy?

(c) How can CAT scans improve the effectiveness of radiotherapy?

(d) Is a patient receiving external radiation therapy, radioactive?

Question 10.2

(a) Is a patient receiving internal radiotherapy, radioactive?

(b) Will a patient still be radioactive after treatment?

Internal radiotherapy

For some types of cancer, a radioactive substance is placed inside the body. **Radioisotope** treatment involves the patient being injected with, or swallowing, a radioactive liquid. For example, radioactive iodine-131 is used to treat thyroid cancer. The iodine is absorbed by the thyroid cancer cells, and delivers a large dose of radiation to them.

Another internal radiotherapy method is **brachytherapy**, where some radioactive material (called the **source**) is implanted in the patient in or close to the tumour to be treated. In some cases this is removed after the treatment period. In other cases the implants will be left in the body and the radiation will gradually fade away.

Planning radiotherapy

Although radiotherapy is less common than diagnostic use of radioactive material in medicine, it is nevertheless widespread, important and growing. An ideal therapeutic radioisotope is a strong beta emitter with just enough gamma to enable imaging e.g. lutenium-177

Planning the treatment:

- How much radiation and to where? Each area is called the *field*.
- There may between one and four beams pointing at the cancer from different angles. Where these beams meet is where the highest dose of radiotherapy is given.

The plan is for the cancer to receive the prescribed dose of radiation while normal body tissue receives as little as possible.

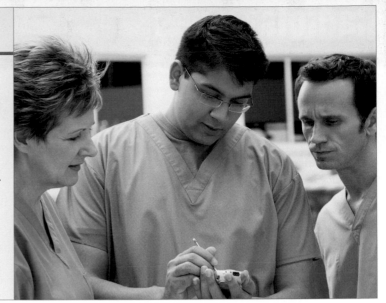

Question 10.3

Match the statements.

the *concentration and area* when planning radiotherapy	glucose
used in radiotherapy	field
treatment uses this radiation	gamma
diagnosis uses this radiation	beta
a chemical used to *fuel* the brain	iodine-131

Biological half-life

The biological half-life is the length of time it takes for the amount of a substance in the body of a living organism to halve.

The biological half-life is a much less precise measure than the physical half-life because there are many physical processes involved. Radioactive half-life is not affected by physical or chemical conditions. Fortunately, living organisms may excrete isotopes so that there is no longer exposure to the radiation.

Examples:

Phosphorous has a long biological half-life (it tends to accumulate within bones) but its short physical half-life minimises exposure.

Tritium clears from the body quickly (short biological half-life) so, even though it has a fairly long physical half-life, the exposure is low.

Effective half-life

When a radioactive substance is put in the body, either for internal radiotherapy or as a tracer, the length of time it stays in the body will depend on both the biological half-life, T_B and the physical half-life, T_P. These two effects will combine to give the effective half-life, T_E:

$$\frac{1}{T_E} + \frac{1}{T_B} = \frac{1}{T_P}$$

The effective half-life will always be shorter than the physical and biological half-lives, as the radioactive and biological processes are working at the same time.

isotope	half-life in days		
	T_P	T_B	T_E
Tritium	4500	12	12
Phosphorous	14.3	1155	14.1
Strontium	11000	18000	6800

Question 10.4

Calculate the effective half-life for technetium, if T_B is 1 day and T_P is 0.2 days

Radioisotopes

Iridium-192

Iridium-192 produces gamma radiation and beta particles as it decays.
Its half-life is 74 days. It is a man-made radioactive element produced from non radioactive iridium metal.

In Brachytherapy Boost Radiation, a needle is inserted where there still might be residual cancer cells after a tumour has been removed. A ribbon of iridium-192 is slid into the hollow needles and then left in for two days to destroy any cancer cells.

Iodine-131

Iodine-131 produces beta and gamma radiation as it decays. Its half-life is eight days.

Stable iodine can be found in seaweed and sponges. The radioactive isotopes of iodine are made by nuclear fission. Radioactive iodine-131 is injected in the bloodstream and then circulated round the body in the blood. Cancer cells will pick up the iodine wherever it is in the body.

This is a targeted treatment and only the thyroid cells pick up iodine.

Cobalt-60

Gamma radiation penetrates and destroys internal tumours. Cobalt-60, the most widely-used isotope, is produced by bombarding Cobalt-59 with neutrons.

The Cobalt-60 nuclei emit gamma radiation with a half-life of five years.

The radioactive Cobalt is contained in a lead-filled steel vessel with a narrow outlet. The source is moved to the outlet when the patient is in position. Because gamma radiation can penetrate more than 1 metre of air without losing strength, the patient can be moved so that the tumour is bombarded from different directions.

Technetium-99m

Technetium-99m is a γ-ray emitting isotope that is often used as a radioactive tracer. It is a synthetic element that decays to technetium-99. It's the most important radionuclide in current use. It's used in 80% of radioactive medical procedures – 40 000 every day.

It emits relatively low frequency radiation which can be detected by gamma cameras and can be combined with a number of different compounds to target different parts of the body. It has a physical half-life (T_P) of ~ 6.03 hours and a biological half-life (T_B) of up to one day. The effective half-life (T_E) is given by:

$1/T_E = 1/T_B + 1/T_R$

$1/T_E = 1/6 + 1/24 = 5/24$

$T_E = 24/5$ hours

This makes the effective half-life 0.2 of a day (slightly less than five hours).

Advantages of technetium-99m

Only emits γ-rays

Easily detected by gamma cameras

Short half-life ~ six hours
- low radiation dose for the patient
- will not ionise remote parts of the body

Versatile
- can concentrate on specific tissues or organs, if used with biologically active substances
- can be used in tracers

Choice of radioisotope

Every organ in our body acts differently from a chemical point of view. There are a number of chemicals which are absorbed by specific organs, such as:
- thyroid – takes up iodine
- brain – consumes large quantities of glucose.

Radioimmunotherapy (RIT)

Specific antibody molecules – which recognise and bind to only one molecular structure – are attached to an isotope that emits γ-rays. They are injected into the bloodstream where they travel around until they find, and bind to, cancer cells. The γ-rays then kill the cancer cells.

RIT is still in clinical trials but might eventually be used for leukaemia, lymphoma (Hodgkin's and non-Hodgkin's) and multiple myeloma.

Question 11.1

(a) What is the difference between biological and physical half-life?

(b) If the biological half-life of a compound of technetium-99m is 12 hours, what is the effective half-life?

(c) Why can there be different values for the biological half-life?

Selecting radioisotopes

Numerous factors need to be considered when selecting a radioisotope to be used in diagnosis or treatment.

Activity

The radioisotope must give off enough of the right kind of radiation (gamma radiation of a frequency which will be detected by the gamma camera) to be useful while doing as little damage as possible.

Effective half-life

Unless the radioisotope is to be removed at a later date, the substance should have a relatively short effective half-life so it doesn't remain in the body for too long. However, the substance should stay long enough for the diagnosis or treatment to be carried out.

Target

Some isotopes, such as technetium-99m, can be combined in different compounds to target different parts of the body; iodine 131 is used for treatment and diagnosis of thyroid problems.

Speed

The speed of radioactive particles is important. Beta particles travel very fast. This, combined with their small size, gives them significant penetrating power.

Question 11.2
Why is gamma radiation favoured in medical imaging techniques?

Diagnosis using radioisotopes

Radioactive substances can be put into the body for diagnosis as part of a compound designed to target the part of the body to be studied (a **tracer**). Once in the body, the gamma radiation given off by the radioisotope is detected by a gamma camera. The gamma camera takes a series of images to show how the tracer moves through the body.

Waste

All radioactive waste – from clothes that have been exposed to radioactive materials, to the materials themselves – must be disposed of following strict regulations.

Medical radiocative waste is often classed as *Low Level Waste*. Isotopes such as technetium-99 have short half-lives and can be left to decay for a period of time and then disposed of with domestic refuse. Some isotopes, such as caesium-137, have longer half-lives and are classed as *Intermediate Level Waste*. These are often shielded and stored underground.

Radioactive tracers - PET scans

A PET (Positron Emission Tomography) scan uses radioactive sugar which is rapidly taken up by fast growing cancer cells. This tracer gives rise to powerful γ-rays which can be seen using a gamma camera. This can be rotated around the patient so that a computer can build up cross sections or a 3D image on a screen.

Uses

Brain activity – using tracers that target neuron activity.

Tumor detection – tracers show active cells indicating aggressiveness of tumors or relapse after treatment.

Detecting inflammation or infection – gallium tracer will indicate location.

Kidney disease – tracers can reveal kidney function.

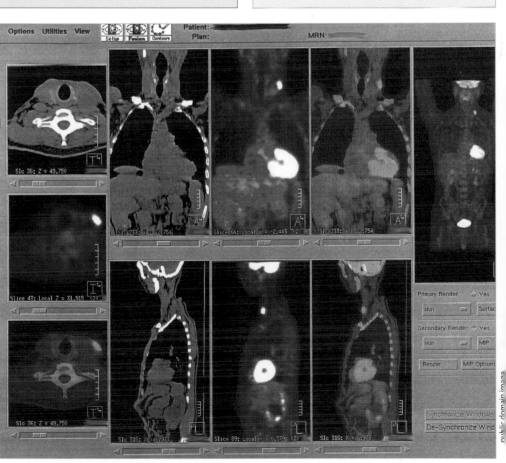

What are X-rays and γ-rays?

X-rays and γ-rays (gamma rays) are types of electromagnetic radiation at the high end of the spectrum (in other words, they have small wavelengths and high frequency).

The longer the wavelength, the lower the frequency and the less energy the wave has (e.g. radio waves).

The shorter the wavelength, the higher the frequency and the more energy the wave has (e.g. gamma radiation).

The frequency ranges of X-rays and γ-rays overlaps. The range of γ-rays extends to higher frequencies.

X-rays and γ-rays can have the same frequency and wavelength, but they are produced differently:

- X-rays are produced by firing electrons at a metal target.
- γ-rays are produced by radioactive sources.

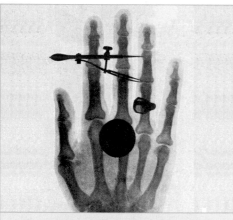

X-ray discovery

In 1895, Röntgen discovered X-rays. He showed that this radiation blackens photographic film. The invisible, but highly penetrating, radiation was previously unknown – hence X-rays. The first *medical* X-ray was of the bones in Röntgen's hand.

Question 12.1

If X-rays have wavelengths of the order of 10^{-10} m or less, what is the corresponding maximum frequency?

X-rays and diagnosis

X-rays are especially useful for examining the chest, bones, joints and abdomen. They are painless and relatively safe to use with people of all ages.

Diagnoses

- Fractured, chipped or dislocated bones
- Evaluating joint injuries and bone infections
- Cancer
- The spread of cancer to other parts of the body (metastasized)
- Diagnosing and monitoring degenerative conditions, such as arthritis or osteoporosis
- Heart and lung disease screening
- Artery blockages
- The cause of chest pains and coughs
- Broken ribs or a punctured lung
- Causes of abdominal pain
- Identify and locate accidentally swallowed objects
- Determine bone or disk injury in the spine
- Spinal defects such as scoliosis (spinal curvature)
- Evaluating sinusitis
- Dental problems and other jaw abnormalities.

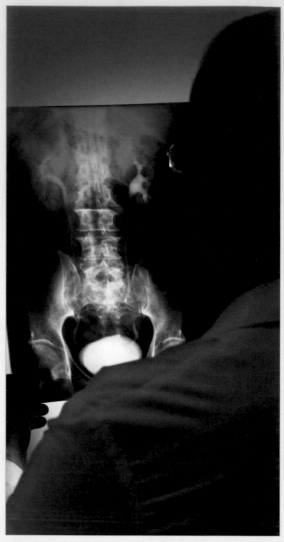

Absorption of X-rays and γ-rays

X-rays and γ-rays can be absorbed by individual atoms. The level of absorption depends on the atomic number (number of protons) of the atoms. Bones contain calcium (atomic number 20) and absorb more X-rays than soft tissue, made of carbon (6), oxygen (8) and hydrogen (1). The amount of absorption will also depend on the thickness of the material that the X-rays pass through, and the density of the material.

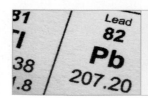

Question 12.2

Why is lead a good material for shielding us from X-rays and γ-rays?

X-ray tubes

X-rays are produced by firing fast-moving electrons at a metal target.

The electrons are produced by a heated filament.

There is a high voltage applied between this (the cathode) and the metal target (the anode) which accelerates the electrons released by the filament towards the target.

The filament and target are enclosed in a vacuum with a lead casing.

The target is angled so that the X-rays can leave the casing through a window.

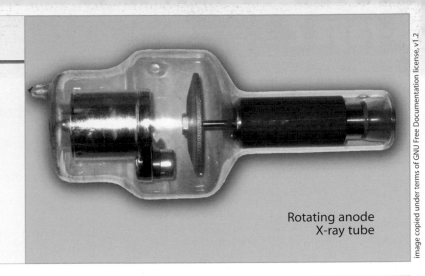

Rotating anode
X-ray tube

image copied under terms of GNU Free Documentation license, v1.2

Question 12.3

Label the diagram with the words:

anode | cathode

electrons | casing

filament | window | target

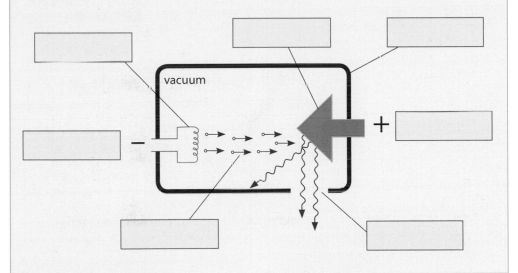

vacuum

Question 12.4

Within the X-ray tube there is a vacuum. Why has all the air been evacuated?

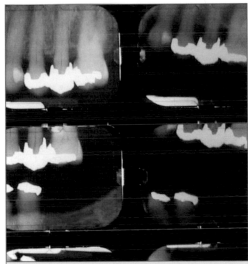

PSPs and dental X-rays

At a hospital, radiation is passed through the body and the image is detected on the other side. In modern hospitals, X-ray sensitive film has been replaced by plates using photostimulatable phosphors (PSPs). Laser stimulation of the PSP plate generates light which is converted to a digital image by computer technology.

At the dentist, the radiation passes through the jaw to the X-ray film inside the mouth.

Question 12.6

(a) *Why are silhouettes of your bones or teeth left on the X-ray film while your skin appears transparent?*

(b) *Why do metal fillings appear so prominently on X-ray film?*

Attenuation

Attenuation – decrease of strength with distance.

X-rays are attenuated as they pass through matter: the intensity of an X-ray beam decreases the farther it penetrates into matter.

Each interaction of an X-ray photon with an atom of the material removes an X-ray from the beam, decreasing its intensity.

The decrease in intensity depends on:

*   The depth of penetration or thickness
*   The material's *absorption coefficient*

Contrast

X-rays are extremely useful as a diagnostic technique because they produce high contrast images. i.e. they enable different areas of the body to show up more clearly.

An X-ray image is formed by the different attenuation of the X-ray beam within a patient's body. Objects with increased attenuation produce shadows.

Question 12.5

If an X-ray finds it easy to penetrate an organ, and so penetration is increased, how will that affect the contrast? Why does a chest X-ray have high contrast?

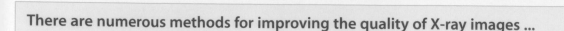

There are numerous methods for improving the quality of X-ray images ...

Sharpness will be improved if the beam of X-rays is narrow.

The diagram shows how a larger source will cause the edges of the shadow case by an object to become blurred:

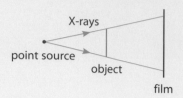
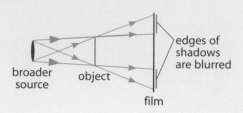

Sharpness can also be improved by changing the relative positions of the source, the object to be X-rayed and the X-ray film:

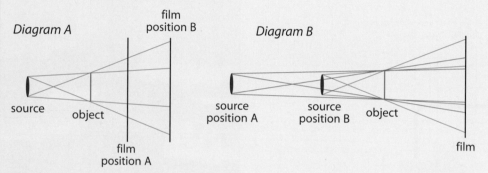

Diagram A

Diagram B

Question 13.1

Look at the two ray diagrams above.

(a) Diagram A shows the effect of changing the film position relative to the object. Which film position will give a sharper picture?

(b) Diagram B shows the effect of changing the position of the source. Which source position will give the sharper picture?

X-rays are produced by firing fast moving electrons at a metal target. The size of the beam will depend on the area of the target being hit by the electrons. The X-ray beam can be made smaller by focusing the electron beam before it hits the target, and by angling the target:

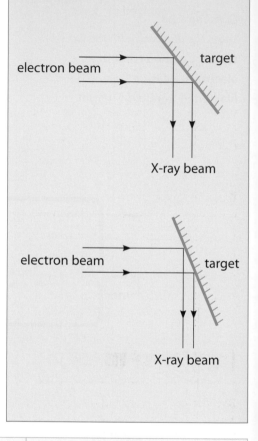

Filtration

X-rays generated by an X-ray tube will have a spectrum of frequencies.

The X-rays at the lower end of the spectrum are more likely to be absorbed or scattered by the patient, and will not make a positive contribution to the image. But they will contribute to the radiation dose the patient receives.

To reduce the amount of these low frequency rays, the X-rays can be passed through a filter. The filter absorbs most of the low frequency rays, but allows the higher frequency rays to pass.

Scattering grid

Some X-rays will be scattered as they pass through the patient. To prevent these scattered rays reaching the film, a grid can be placed between the patient and the film. The grid is aligned to allow rays from the X-ray source to reach the film, but reduce the number of scattered rays which reach the film. The grid does decrease the number of X-rays reaching the film, so exposure may need to be increased.

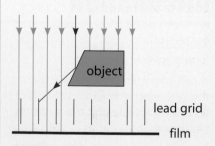

The lead grid allows most of the direct rays through, but stops most scattered rays (shown in pink).

Movement blur

Any movement will blur the image. Movements can be involuntary, for example movement of the internal organs. In such cases the exposure time has to be kept short.

Detection

There are two main methods for detecting X-rays: **fluorescence and photographic film.**

Fluoroscopy

Fluorescent screens absorb X-rays, then re-emit some of the energy as visible light. A high dose of X-rays are required to view this directly. In the past, the radiographer would have to sit in a darkened room. Now image intensifiers are used, so the image can be viewed on a TV screen, or saved digitally. Fluoroscopy has the advantage of being able to look at images which change with time. Fluorescent screens are also used to improve film photography.

Fluoroscopy usually involves more exposure to X-rays than conventional radiography because the exposure time is longer.

Fluoroscope

Contrast

- Different areas of the body absorb X-rays by different amounts
- Different tissues have different densities
- Suitable energy X-rays are used (different kV values can change the spectrum)
- Use of **contrast media**

Contrast media

Because several types of tissue absorb X-rays by similar amounts, there is very little contrast between them.

Contrast media with a high atomic number can be used to distinguish between them.

Iodine is injected into blood vessels to study blood flow.

A suspension of barium sulfate can be used to study the digestion system.

This can be taken orally – either as a **barium swallow** (used when obtaining X-ray images of the throat and gullet), a **barium meal** (used when taking images of the stomach), or a **barium follow-through** (used when looking at the small intestine).

A **barium enema** is used for imaging of the colon.

Question 13.4

Are contrast media radioactive?

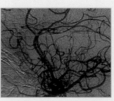

An angiogram: iodine is injected into blood vessels.

A barium swallow: the patient swallows barium liquid and it flows through the oesophagus and into the stomach. X-rays are taken to look for abnormal areas.

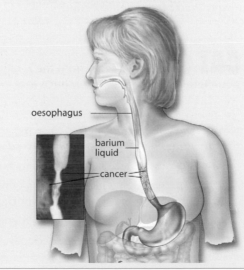

oesophagus

barium liquid

cancer

Photographic film

Photographic film is not very sensitive to X-rays. Most of the rays pass through the film. Image intensifying screens are used to improve the quality of the image, and reduce the X-ray dose the patient receives. The image intensifying screens form a reusable cassette which encloses the photographic film. Using more sensitive X-ray emulsions can also allow the dose to be reduced.

Question 13.2

The diagram shows a film cassette. Label the different layers.

A white plastic

B cassette front - plastic

C base

D cassette back - metal

E fluorescent layer

F film emulsion

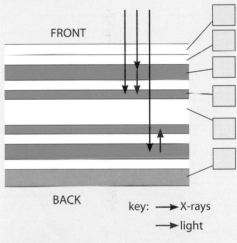

FRONT

BACK

key: → X-rays

→ light

Question 13.3

(a) What two types of radiation produce the image?

(b) What are the sources of the radiation?

(c) Which of these makes the largest contribution to the image?

(d) Why is the use of image intensifying screens good for safety?

X-ray film cassette

Computed Axial Tomography (CAT) scans

Computed Axial Tomography (CAT) and Computerised Tomography (CT) are the same thing.

Conventional X-rays only give two dimensional images. These images are *shadow* images. This means that all depths are superimposed on each other so, for example, a large bone may hide a smaller one.

CAT scans (also known as CT scans) also use X-rays, but the X-rays pass through the patient in many different directions. The information this produces is processed by computers to generate 2D slices through the body and/or 3D images.

The X-ray tube produces a fan-shaped beam which is detected by a curved row of sensitive detectors. The source and detectors are rotated around the body. The diagram shows a cross section of a CAT scanner for the source and detectors in two different positions. It shows that the shadow cast by the object depends on the direction of the beam. The computer can take the information generated by the detectors and process it to reconstruct the cross-section in great detail.

To obtain 3D information, the patient is moved through the detector so that several slices can be recorded. These can then be combined to turn the data into a 3D rotatable image.

These two pictures show the image of a skull constructed from a number of 'slices'.

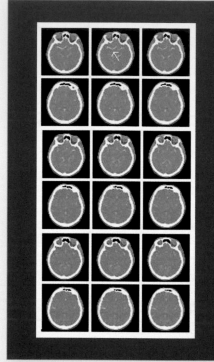

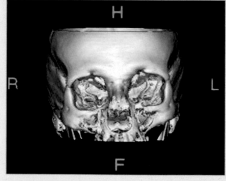

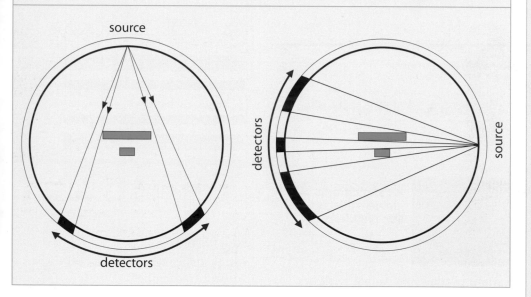

Question 14.1

Why will a CAT scan involve more exposure to X-rays than conventional X-rays?

The pros and cons of CAT scans

PROS	CONS
• can be used to image soft tissues, for example the brain • can show cross-sections or 3D images • often more quickly available than MRI in the UK • provide better **clarity** than conventional X-rays for internal organs, bone, soft tissue, like the brain, and blood vessels	• more ionising radiation • may not distinguish scar tissue from active cancerous tissue • involves being confined in a small space – may be problematic for claustrophobic patients • much more expensive than conventional X-rays • requires a cooperative or sedated patient

Scanning

The patient is usually lying flat on their back but may be on their side or their stomach, on the CAT examination table. To hold the patient still, in the correct position, straps and pillows may be used.

If a contrast material is needed, it will be swallowed, injected through an intravenous line or administered by enema, depending on the type of examination.

When in position, the table will move slowly through the scanner.

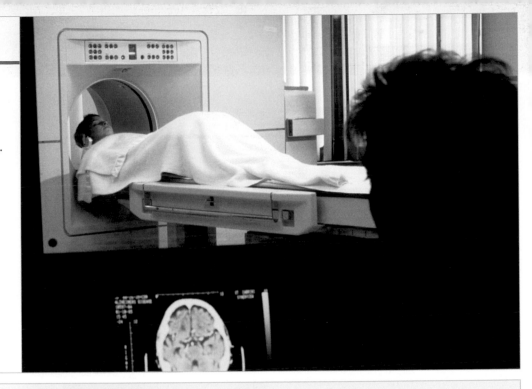

Question 14.2

(a) Why might the patient be asked to hold their breath during the scanning?

(b) Why might an extremely obese person not be able to have a CAT scan?

Spiral CAT Scan

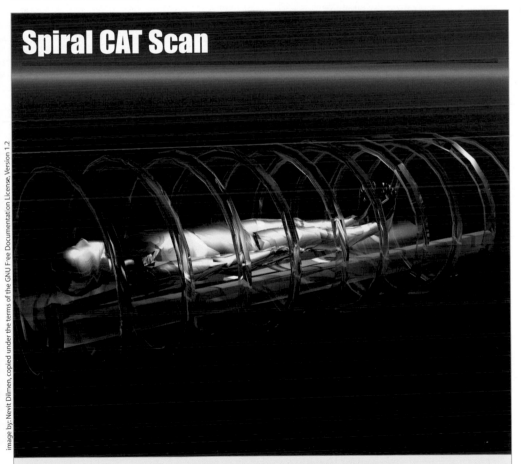

This is a newer type of CAT scanner, also known as a helical scanner.

It is called a spiral scanner because the X-ray beam moves in a spiral around the patient. In practice, instead of the couch being *stepped* through the scanner, the couch moves continuously while the X-ray source rotates.

A helical scanner works faster than a standard scanner and gives more detailed pictures.

Uses of CAT Scans

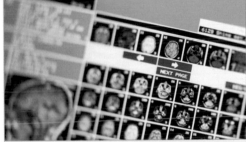

As well as bones, CAT scans can be used to view soft tissues, internal organs and even blood vessels.

CAT scans are often used on the head and the abdomen. They can be used to diagnose tumours, the swelling of arteries and bleeding in the brain. CAT scans can diagnose conditions of internal organs and identify tears (lacerations) of the spleen, liver or kidney.

Because CAT scans can identify abnormal tissue, they can be used for planning radiotherapy, and as a guide for taking tissue and cell samples for examination (biopsies). They can also be used in preparation for surgery.

They can be used for looking at bones, especially the spine, and assessing bone density when investigating osteoporosis (a condition which causes thinning and weakening of the bones).

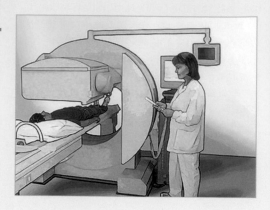

Gamma cameras

A gamma camera detects γ-rays.

The camera uses a layer of crystal which gives off a flash of light each time a gamma photon strikes it. Photodetectors detect when and where these flashes occur.

The γ-rays emitted by a radioactive tracer will come off the body in all directions. To make an image where a point in the image relates directly to a point in the body (as a result, improving spatial resolution) a **collimator** is used. The collimator is usually a sheet of lead 3-8 cm thick with thousands of small holes through it. The γ-rays entering the collimator in the direction of these holes will be able to pass through and reach the crystal. The lead will stop most of the other rays, reducing the sensitivity of the gamma camera.

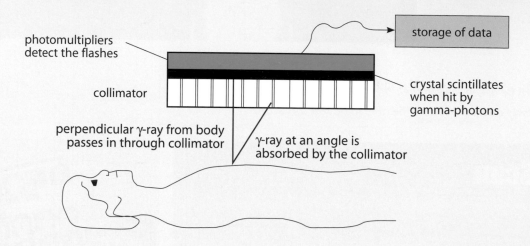

photomultipliers detect the flashes

storage of data

collimator

crystal scintillates when hit by gamma-photons

perpendicular γ-ray from body passes in through collimator

γ-ray at an angle is absorbed by the collimator

Rectilinear scanner

Rectilinear scanners produce a two–dimensional image showing the distribution of a radioisotope. The patient is scanned in a *rectilinear* motion. In other words, in a series of staight lines, back and forth.

The detector (a scintillator which detects gamma radiation) produces output pulses. It is connected via an electronic circuit to a light bulb which moves across a photographic film in the same motion as the detector. The intensity of light from the bulb increases as more γ-rays are detected. The greater the intensity of light, the darker the photographic film becomes. Thus, an image is built up, line by line.

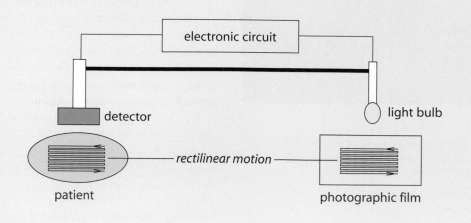

electronic circuit

detector

light bulb

rectilinear motion

patient

photographic film

Rectilinear v gamma camera

Rectilinear scanners were invented in 1950. They were better than their predecessor – the Geiger tube – which only gave a crude indication of the distribution of a radiosotope.

However, only six years later the gamma camera was invented.

It could capture an entire organ at once, it was much quicker than the rectilinear scanner (which could take more than half an hour), and the images captured were of a higher resolution.

Rectilinear scanners were also subject to *motion artifacts*. Although people could remain still while being scanned, it wasn't possible for them to control the movement of their internal organs. The lungs, for example, move up and down 2 cm during normal breathing.

Geiger tubes

A Geiger tube is a device for counting atomic particles, named after German physicist Hans Geiger. Gas between electrodes is ionised by the passage of a particle, and so transmits a pulse to a counter.

- The Geiger tube is sealed and contains argon gas at low pressure.
- The thin mica window at the end of the tube allows alpha and beta particles to enter from outside.
- Gamma radiation can enter via the mica and also the walls of the tube.
- A metal rod in the middle of the tube is given a positive potential.
- The walls of the tube are connected to the negative terminal of the supply.

When a radioactive particle enters the tube:

- the particle ionises gas atoms along its track
- these atoms become ions
- some are positively charged and some are negatively charged.

Question 15.1

(a) Which ions or particles are attracted to the anode and which to the cathode?

(b) What is the pulse counter actually measuring?

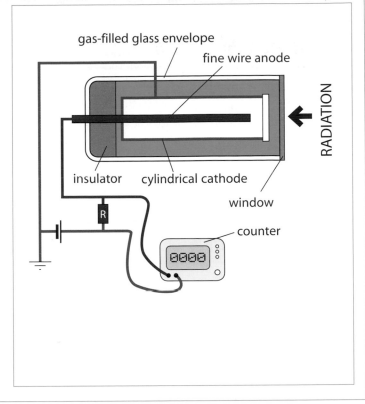

Film badges

People who work with radiation wear film badges. They're a type of dosimeter – they measure the amount of radiation (X-rays, beta particles and γ-rays) that the wearer is exposed to.

The detector is a piece of radiation sensitive film. The film goes darker when it absorbs radiation – the more radiation, the darker it becomes. It is packaged in casing to prevent light, moisture or chemical vapours from affecting the film.

Inside the casing there are filters which the radiation has to penetrate before reaching the film. The filters attenuate different types of radiation, so only the target radiation is monitored. There is also an open *window*.

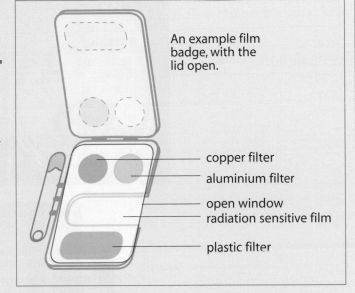

An example film badge, with the lid open.

- copper filter
- aluminium filter
- open window
- radiation sensitive film
- plastic filter

Question 15.2

Why do film badges not measure alpha particles?

Question 15.3

(a) Is the use of a gamma camera invasive or non-invasive?

(b) X-ray images show bone and other tissue mass. What do γ-ray images reveal?

(c) A radioisotope is administered to the patient before the images are taken. Why?

PET

Positron emission tomography produces high quality, 3D colour images.

The scanner is a sophisticated device incorporating gamma cameras.

Positron emissions from the ingested radioisotope show up as different colours and brightness on a PET image.

PET scans are used for diagnosis to find out how a condition is developing or how well treatment is working.

- detecting cancer, assessing its spread and checking if its returned
- assess the effectiveness of therapy
- assess blood flow to the heart
- find out the effects of a heart attack
- identify heart muscle that would benefit from surgery
- brain scans relating to tumours, memory loss, seizures and central nervous system disorders.

PET scans are often used in conjunction with CAT scans to pinpoint diseases.

Disadvantages:

- γ-rays harmful
- doesn't show slow growing cancers well
- PET scans are expensive
- can't be used if breast feeding.

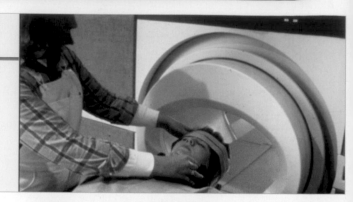

What is an MRI scan?

Magnetic resonance imaging uses magnetic and radio waves.
No hazardous radiation is involved.

MRI scanners

The scanner comprises

- large cylindrical magnet
- radio wave transmitter
- coils which create magnetic gradients across three axes to control the strength, speed and position of the imaging.

When a patient lies inside the magnet, their hydrogen nuclei (i.e. protons, found in the human body as water) align with the strong magnetic field, forcing the protons into a different position. As they move back into their natural alignment they produce a magnetic field. Different tissues realign at different speeds and so they can be identified separately.

The scanner picks up the signals and a computer turns them into a picture.

Images

Images are made slice by slice through the part of the body being scanned.

Often, contrast agents are injected to enhance the image of tumours etc. They work by altering the local magnetic field in the particular tissue.

The tissue that has the least hydrogen atoms (such as bone) turns out dark, while the tissue that has many hydrogen atoms (such as fatty tissue) looks much brighter.

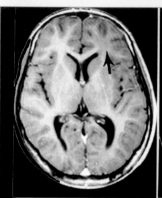
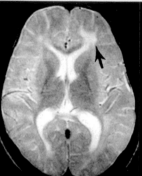
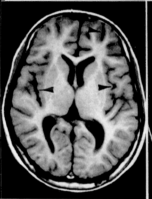
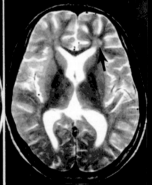

Scans

Almost all tissues in the body can be imaged. Changing the timing of the radio wave pulses gives information about the different types of tissues that are present.

Scans provide clear pictures of areas surrounded by bone tissue, so are useful when examining the brain and spinal cord.

The detailed quality of the images makes it valuable for examining the brain:

- for tumours
- for tumour spread into nearby brain tissue
- examining abnormal tissue in patients with multiple sclerosis
- to monitor bleeding in the brain
- after a stroke.

In addition, MRI scans can show

- heart defects in children
- changes around the heart following a heart attack
- joints and spine
- soft parts of the body such as the liver, kidneys and spleen.

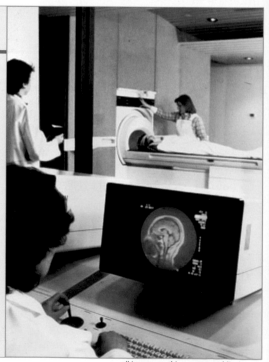

Performing an MRI scan

The scan is usually an outpatient procedure: the patient can go home after the test. During the scan it is important to lie completely still – children might be given an anaesthetic.

Patients are exposed to a powerful magnetic field during the MRI scan, so must not wear jewellery or any other metal objects.

Medical staff check patients for hearing aids, pacemakers or any metal in their body such as surgical clips. Artificial hips or bone screws are not normally a problem.

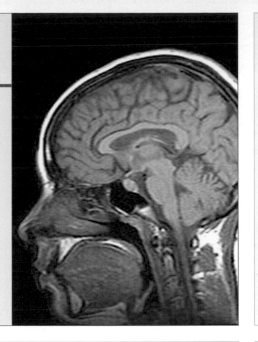

Dangers

There are no known dangers or side effects with MRI scans. It's not painful; you can't feel it. Since radiation is not used, the procedure can be repeated without problems. A fetus during its first twelve weeks may be at risk so scans are not performed on pregnant women during this time.

Patients lie inside a large cylinder during the scan and this may make people feel claustrophobic. Staff can give medication to help them relax.

The machine also makes a banging noise while it is working, which might be unpleasant.

Advantages

- strong magnetic fields and weak radio waves not thought to be harmful
- can visualise soft tissue, especially around bones and joints
- can make 3D image

Disadvantages

- expensive
- needs special facilities to house equipment
- some people feel claustrophobic or are disturbed by the knocking sound during the scan

Best suited for …

examination of internal organs, such as brain, heart and spinal cord – complex 3D images can be produced.

Also:

- sports injuries – soft tissue around dense bone can be seen
- cancer detection – tumours visualised
- reproductive organ examination – no harmful X-rays are used.

MRI and CAT scans

CAT scans	MRI scans
• give excellent information on anatomical features and tissue density	• no known health risks
• detect calcium deposits, cysts and abscesses	• can take pictures from almost every angle
• can be used instead of ultrasound, (obese patients have excess fat that hinders ultrasonic waves)	• not usually suitable for patients with pacemakers, aneurysm clips, or similar
• risks with X-rays, although this is less than for ordinary X-rays	• can examine the central nervous system (brain and spinal cord)
• only shows pictures horizontally	• difference between normal and abnormal tissue is clearer than in a CAT scan
	• much more expensive than CAT scans

Question 16.1

(a) The correct name for MRI is nuclear magnetic resonance imaging. Why nuclear?

(b) Why must radiologists ensure that there are no magnetic objects in the scanner room?

(c) Why might an MRI scan be dangerous if the patient has a stray metal fragment in their body?

(d) A scanner has been developed that allows patients to sit up during the scan. Why might this be helpful?

Ultrasound

Ultrasound

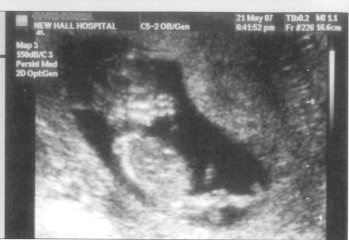

High frequency sound waves beyond the range of the human ear (>20 000 Hz) – **Ultrasonic**

Sound waves within the range of the human ear (20-20 kHz) – **Sonic**

Sound waves with a frequency lower than 20 kHz – **Subsonic**

Ultrasound with very high-frequency acoustic energy, between 1 and 3 MHz is used – **Medical ultrasound**

Q&A

Why is this high frequency noise not heard by the baby during a pre-natal scan?
The frequency is in the ultrasound region. The human ear will not actually hear the sound.

What feature of the wave allows a very sharp image to be recorded?
The small wavelength.

A cycling specialist has claimed that there is a reason why dogs are prone to chasing moving bicycles, even though the bikes appear to make very little noise. Why?
It is believed that the rotating spokes make a noise in the ultrasound region that dogs can hear, but we can't.

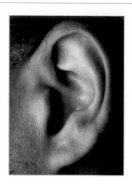

Question 17.1

The frequency range for an average human ear is between 20 000 and 20 Hz.

What are the corresponding wavelengths for these frequencies?

Ultrasound imaging

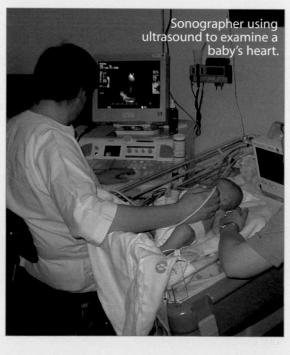

Sonographer using ultrasound to examine a baby's heart.

Ultrasound is used to obtain images of internal parts of the body.

A transmitter sends ultrasound pulses into the body. Good contact with the skin is needed.

Surfaces within the body reflect the sound with different echoes from parts that have a different structure or density.

The time delay of the echoes gives the depths within the body of the reflecting surfaces.

This can be used to build up an image of something inside.

Ultrasound:

- can detect differences between soft tissues which X-rays cannot
- can continuously monitor fetal movement or a person's heart
- can show tumours or lumps inside the body
- can measure the depth of an object below the body surface
- is much safer than X-rays.

public domain image

Acoustic impedance

The speed of sound in air is much less than that in water (and the human body is mostly water).

This means that there is an acoustic impedance difference between the air and the body.

When a sound wave changes media, the ratio of the acoustic impedances of the media determines the efficiency of the energy transfer.

For instance:

The acoustic impedance of the eardrum corresponds well with that of the auditory canal, guaranteeing maximum efficiency of energy transfer. but it does not correspond well with air.

The pinna (part of the ear outside the head) is an impedance matching device between the air and the auditory canal.

Question 17.2

The difference between the speed of ultrasound in air and the body normally means a large part of the ultrasound energy is reflected away from the body and wasted.

(a) What is applied to the skin in order to reduce this?

(b) This is an example of impedance matching. What does this mean and what exactly happens to the ultrasound?

Wavelength

Sound waves are pressure waves. Particles are compressed in high pressure areas. Where particles are spread apart – rarefaction – the pressure is low. The wavelength is the distance between two successive high pressure pulses.

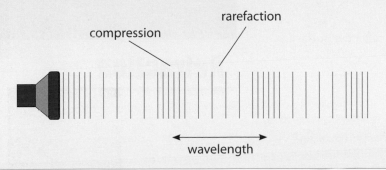

Ultrasound in different materials

medium	speed of ultrasound / m s⁻¹	acoustic impedance / kg m⁻² s⁻¹
air	330	0.000 04
water	1484	1.48
blood	1550	1.61
liver	1570	1.65
fat	1450	1.38
skull bone	3366	5.69

Question 17.3

Choose two media that would give:

(a) greatest energy loss through reflection

(b) smallest energy loss through reflection.

Ultrasound therapy

Ultrasound can transfer energy to locations within the body. It is thought to be low risk and is non invasive. Specific frequencies are delivered for a measured time.

Sound energy is transformed to heat, giving a warming effect for soft tissues and joints, to reduce inflammation, increase blood flow, ease pain and stiffness.

Sound energy is transformed to kinetic energy, for breaking up

- gall stones and kidney stones, to reduce their size so that they can pass out of the body naturally; this is lithotripsy
- the cloudy lens in cataract surgery
- fibroids
- tumours; a new technique where an MRI scanner is used to direct the ultrasound.

Speed

Ultrasound speed

- depends on what material or tissue it is travelling through
- depends on how closely the particles are spaced, their mass and the attracting force between them
- does not depend on its frequency.

Frequency

Ultrasound is reflected at the boundaries between different materials. Ultrasound reflects very well wherever soft tissue meets air, or soft tissue meets bone, or where bone meets air.

Frequency is unchanged as sound travels through various tissues. In tissues where sound travels more slowly, wavelength decreases.

Remember the **wave equation**:

velocity = frequency x wavelength

Intensity reflection coefficients

Ultrasonic waves are reflected at boundaries where there is a difference in acoustic impedances (Z) of the materials on each side of the boundary.

This difference in Z is the impedance mismatch. The greater the impedance mismatch, the greater the percentage of energy reflected at the interface (boundary) between one medium and another.

Particle velocity and local particle pressures must be continuous across the boundary. So, we can find what fraction of the incident wave intensity is refracted. The reflection coefficient, α, at a boundary is given by

$$\left(\frac{Z_1 - Z_2}{Z_1 + Z_2}\right)^2$$

Z_1 and Z_2 are the acoustic impedances of the two media.

α x 100 gives the reflected energy as a percentage of the original energy.

Law of reflection

When a ray of light hits a reflective surface, for example a mirror, the angle of incidence equals the angle of reflection.

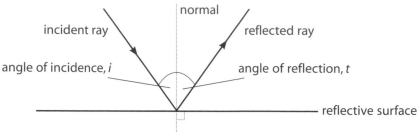

Question 18.1

Match the terms with their definitions ...

angle of incidence	a construction line at right angles to the surface at the point where the incident ray hits the surface
normal	the angle that the reflected ray makes with the normal, equal to the angle of incidence
angle of reflection	the angle that the incoming ray makes with the normal

Refraction

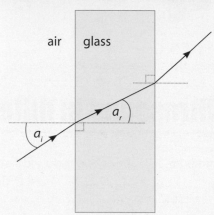

When a ray of light moves from one medium to another, the speed and direction of the ray will change. The amount of change will depend on the **refractive index, *n*.**

$$n = \frac{\text{velocity of light in air}}{\text{velocity of light in medium}}$$

This is Snell's Law.

If a ray is travelling into a medium with a **higher** refractive index, for example from air into glass, the light will be bent **towards** the normal. If a_i is the angle of incidence and a_r is the angle of refraction, then

$$n = \frac{\sin a_i}{\sin a_r}$$

When the light travels into a medium with a **lower** refractive index, for example from glass into air, the light will be bent **away** from the normal.

The refractive index depends on the frequency of the light. This is how a prism can split white light into its constituent colours.

Total internal reflection

If a light ray encounters a boundary between the medium it is travelling in and a medium with a lower refractive index, it may be **totally internally reflected**.

Question 18.2

The table below shows values of refractive index. From these values, which of these boundaries can cause total internal reflection?

(a) **air to glass** _____

(b) **glass to air** _____

(c) **diamond to water** _____

(d) **water to glass** _____

(e) **water to air** _____

air	n = 1
water	n = 1.33
glass	n = 1.51
diamond	n = 2.42

Total internal reflection occurs when the angle of incidence to the boundary is greater than the **critical angle.**

The critical angle, θ_c is related to the refractive index of the material by the equation:

$$\sin \theta_c = 1 \div n$$

Question 18.3

(a) What is the critical angle of
(i) water
(ii) diamond?

(b) In the cases shown here, will total internal reflection occur?

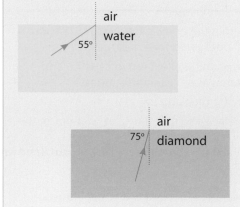

Real and apparent depth

If you look at an object in water, it appears to be less deep than it actually is.

This is because the light rays are refracted as they travel through the boundary between water and air.

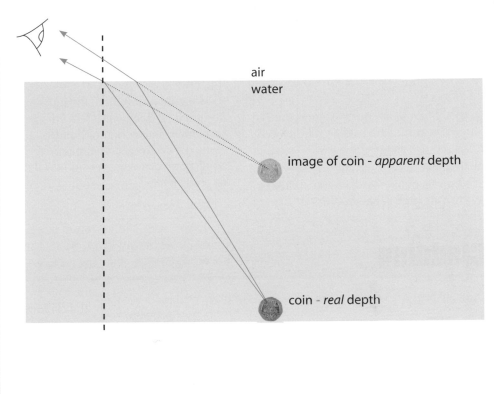

air
water

image of coin - *apparent* depth

coin - *real* depth

A crooked chopstick?

This shows how rays from the chopstick tip are refracted away from the normal when they emerge from the water.

Some of these rays reach the observer's eyes. The eyes are tricked into thinking that they come from where they were redirected. So the tip of the chopstick appears shallower and the chopstick bent.

Question 18.4

The diagram shows a ray of light passing from air to another medium. Fill in the blanks.

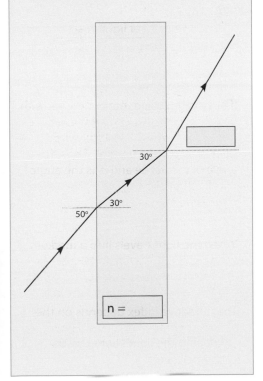

30°

30°

50°

n =

Question 18.5

(a) A student has performed an experiment to determine the critical angle of glass. As part of the experiment she has drawn a diagram, as shown.

Label the diagram and calculate the critical angle, the refractive index of the glass, and the speed of light in the glass. Chose from these words:

incident ray | normal | totally internally reflected ray | glass block

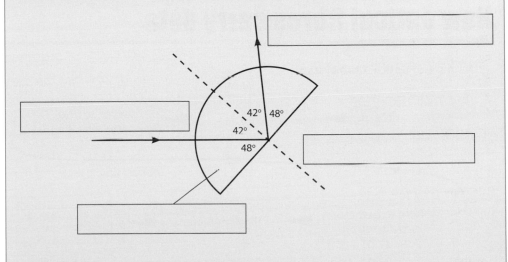

42° 48°

42°

48°

(b) Why does the ray of light not bend when it enters the curved glass block?

(c) Why is total internal reflection only possible when a ray is passing from a material with a higher refractive index to one with a lower refractive index?

Fibre optics

Fibre optics makes use of total internal reflection to guide light along transparent fibres, even though the fibres might be twisted and bent.

At a bend in the fibre, the light rays reflect totally internally off the sides of the fibre.

So the light rays are guided along the fibre. Fibre optics are used in medicine to view the inside of the body.

An image formed by a lens on the end of a bundle of fibres will be transmitted to the other end of the bundle.

Optical fibre cables

Optical fibres are usually bundled together in cables. In a **coherent** bundle, the fibres are arranged in the same order at both ends. This means that an image can be viewed through the bundle, or data can be sent.

In an **incoherent** bundle the individual fibres are randomly ordered. An image sent down an incoherent bundle would be scrambled. The main application of an incoherent bundle is to guide light.

Cladding

Optical fibres are very thin, flexible strands of glass.

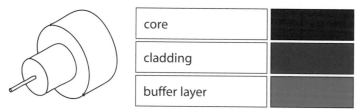

core	
cladding	
buffer layer	

Question 19.1

Colour the diagram to match the key

The cladding has a **lower** refractive index than the core.

Light waves travel along the core of the optical fibre. When the light rays hit the boundary between the core and the cladding, there is **total internal reflection**. This means that the light cannot escape from the core, even if the optical fibre is bent.

The glass fibre is covered in a plastic **buffer layer** which protects the fibre from physical damage.

Question 19.2

What would happen to the light as it passed along a bundle of fibres if they didn't have cladding?

How optical fibres carry data

Diagram of optical fibre system

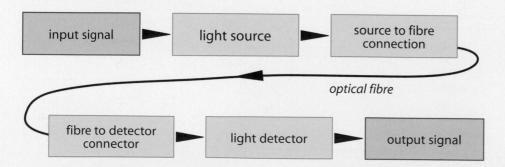

An optical fibre system consists of a light source connected to an optical fibre.

Digital data arives at the light source as an electrical signal. It is usually sent down the fibre by switching the light source on to represent a 1, and off to represent a 0.

Types of optical fibre

Question 19.3
The diagram shows three types of optical fibre. Label each fibre as either:
   single-mode *or* **multimode,** *and either* **step index** *or* **graded index.**

input light pulse	refractive index, n	fibre cross-section	light path along fibre	output light pulse
(a)	50 – 100 μm			
(b)	50 – 85 μm			
(c)	7 – 10 μm			

Multimode fibres

In multimode fibres the light can take many different routes through the fibre. The lengths of these paths will not be the same, so all the light will not arrive at the detector at the same time, resulting in pulse broadening. The longer the fibre is, the greater difference there will be in the lengths of the light paths, so the more the pulse will spread. As a result, there is a trade-off between length of fibre and the data rates that can be transmitted – the longer the fibre, the lower the data rates have to be.

Graded index fibres overcome this problem by having a refractive index which changes gradually at the boundary between the core and the cladding.

Multimode graded fibres have higher bandwidth and/or can transmit over longer distances. They are used in modern telecommunications.

Single mode fibres

In single mode fibres, the light can only take one route down the fibre, which means there is less pulse broadening. They are used for high-data rate, long distance systems. Because the core is so small, single mode cables need high precision connectors and highly directional light sources. Single mode fibres have a very small acceptance angle. They are usually used with high power lasers. Single mode systems will usually be more expensive than multimode systems.

Endoscopy advantages

- Minimally invasive diagnostic tool
- Minimally invasive surgery (biopsies, removal of foreign objects)
- Relatively painless or mildly uncomfortable (usually an aesthesia spray can be used to assist)

Question 19.4
(a) Through an endoscope, the medical professional can carry out biopsies of any abnormal looking tissue. What is a biopsy?
(b) An endoscope is an invasive technique. Give two disadvantages of this type of surgery.

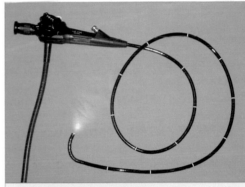

photo copied under terms of GNU Free Documentation License, Version 1.2

Endoscopy

Endoscopy uses light to look inside the body. A fibre-optic endoscope consists of a tube containing two bundles of optical fibres, one coherent and one incoherent (and possibly instruments for performing medical procedures, e.g.taking samples). The coherent bundle of fibres is used to carry the image of the inside of the body cavity to a monitor or eyepiece. The incoherent bundle is used to carry light into the body cavity.

Endoscopy uses

- gastrointestinal tract
- respiratory tract
- urinary tract
- the female reproductive system
- closed body cavities through a small incision (keyhole surgery)
- abdominal cavities
- interior of joints
- organs of the chest
- foetus during pregnancy

Lasers

Light Amplification by Stimulated Emission of Radiation.

When energy is pumped into the laser material, its atoms are raised to a higher energy level. As they fall back to their original energy level, they emit photons. If it hits another atom, another photon is emitted which is exactly in phase with the first. These two photons then produce two more and so on. This amplification leads to a beam of light where all the photons are in phase and travelling in the same direction. The stream is focused into a narrow beam of high intensity light.

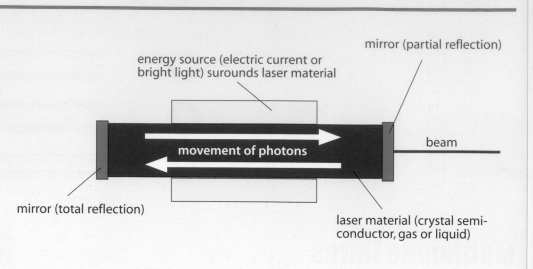

energy source (electric current or bright light) surrounds laser material

mirror (partial reflection)

movement of photons

beam

mirror (total reflection)

laser material (crystal semi-conductor, gas or liquid)

Question 20.1

How does laser light compare with ordinary light? Fill the gaps using these words.

microns | parallel | mixed | laser | spreads | coherent | controlled | single | less

(a) White light is a mix of colours with _____ wavelengths.

(b) Laser light is monochromatic with a _____ wavelength. It is _____. These identical

waves travel _____ to one another.

(c) _____ light travels as a tight beam.

(d) Ordinary light _____ out, so _____ light hits a given area as it travels away from its source.

(e) The strong parallel laser beam can be focused to a few _____ in diameter.

(f) Laser light can be _____ precisely, in a continuous beam, in bursts or in pulses.

Lasers in cancer treatment

may be used to

- relieve symptoms such as bleeding or obstruction
- shrink or destroy a tumour that is blocking a patient's trachea (windpipe) or oesophagus
- remove tumours that are blocking the colon or stomach.

Laser therapy can be used alone, but most often it is combined with other treatments, such as surgery, chemotherapy or radiation therapy.

Laser-induced interstitial thermotherapy

LITT – laser-induced interstitial thermotherapy (or interstitial laser photocoagulation): light energy is converted to heat. When delivered to a tumour, this heat will damage or kill the cancer cells and shrink the tumour.

Laser therapy

is often given through a flexible endoscope. It is inserted through an opening in the body, such as the mouth, nose, anus, or vagina. Laser light is then precisely aimed to cut or destroy a tumour.

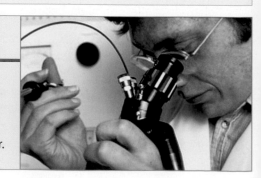

Photodynamic therapy

is a method for destroying cancer cells. It uses light sensitive drugs which only become active when exposed to light of the correct frequency. When administered to the body they are attracted to the cancer cells, and become concentrated in them. When light from a laser is shone on the area, the drug becomes active and destroys the cells where it is concentrated. An incoherent bundle of optical fibres are often used to target the laser light onto the correct area.

Lasers can be used in a variety of ways:

- fixing a detached retina
- sealing nerve endings to reduce pain after surgery
- sealing wounds
- corneal surgery
- cosmetic surgery.

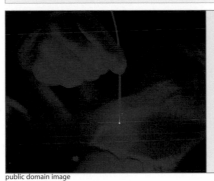

public domain image

Question 20.2

In the photo, left, a surgeon is treating an area with light from a laser.

Why is the picture lit with red light?

Pros and cons of laser therapy

PROS	CONS
• More precise than scalpels, so do less damage to normal tissue • Simplify many surgical procedures • There is less pain, bleeding, swelling, scarring • Operations shorter • Can be done on an outpatient basis • Takes less time for patients to heal • Patients less likely to get infections • Increases the range of treatable conditions	• Surgeons must have specialised training • Strict safety precautions must be followed • It is expensive • The equipment is bulky • The effects may not last long, so treatment may have to be repeated

Laparoscopic Surgery

keyhole or *minimal access* surgery

Laparoscopic surgery is an alternative to traditional open surgery. Open surgery requires large incisions to allow the surgeon's hands to enter. Laparoscopic surgery is performed through small incisions.

A number of 'ports' are used. These allow access to the diseased organ and a telescope for the surgeon to see inside the body. Instruments are placed through additional ports. Surgeons can see what they are doing on a high resolution monitor whilst carrying out the procedure.

Question 20.3

Sort this list into advantages / disadvantages of laparoscopic surgery.

- **No large incisions needed**
- **More often a longer operation**
- **Bleeding infection at the 'port' site**
- **Less pain**
- **Shorter convalescence**
- **Higher level of skill required by the surgeon**
- **Avoids open surgery and the resulting scar**
- **Loss of tactile information**
- **Shorter hospital stay**

How it's done

The laparoscope (fibre-optic camera) is inserted through an incision approximately 1 cm long. Depending on the operation further small incisions are made to allow access for the instruments. In each of these incisions a plastic tube, called a *port*, is inserted to allow laparoscopes / instruments to be moved in and out.

Only three or four ports are opened for minor surgery, such as hernia repairs, gallstone surgery or appendectomy. For major surgery four or five ports are used.

Laser dangers

Lasers cause burns.

Serious hazards are explosions and fire, particularly during surgery on the airway (the endotracheal tube): the high oxygen concentrations and the laser (a high energy ignition source) are close together.

Not all existing treatments are available to all people

In November 2006 news broke that Fraser, the son of Gordon Brown (then Chancellor of the Exchequer) had cystic fibrosis.

At that time, under the NHS, only certain areas of the UK automatically tested newborn children for the condition. Treatments and tests vary in availability, according to priorities set by the health service.

For many reasons, there are regional variations in the treatments that patients can receive and the lengths of waiting lists.

Risk factors

Most treatments have side effects.

The benefits of treatment have to be weighed up against the potential risks.

Is there a risk that

- the patient will die or be severely handicapped as a result of treatment (for example, an old person may not be fit enough to undertake a major operation under a general anaesthetic)?
- the patient's quality of life may be badly affected?
- the patient may be allergic to the drug?
- the patient may be exposed to excessive amounts of radiation, if they undergo too many tests or prolonged treatment?

Personal factors

Religious, cultural or personal values and beliefs can affect which treatments are acceptable to people.

For example pro-life groups believe that human life starts at fertilisation. So, abortion for *any* reason is not acceptable.

Jehovah's Witnesses believe that blood transfusions act against the word of the Bible.

Ethical factors

Ethics enter into any decision where a value judgement or moral decision has to be made.

The question is:

'Is this the right decision under the circumstances?'

The potential benefit to the patient has to be taken into account.

Difficult decisions can include:

'Should I choose very painful treatment and longer life or a peaceful but shorter life?'

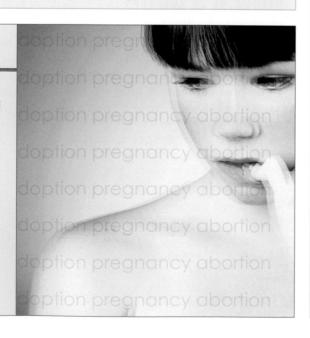

Financial factors

In the UK, the watchdog on medicines is the National Institute for Clinical Excellence (NICE). It was set up to promote the cost-effective use of drugs by the NHS.

NICE is responsible for approving drugs for use in the UK. They take risk factors (see *Risk factors*) and financial factors into account.

NHS Trusts protested when NICE approved the use of the breast cancer drug Herceptin because the cost is about £20 000 per woman for a year's treatment. They were worried that they would have to cut other treatments to pay for it.

Newbury and Community Primary Care Trust appealed against the decision on the grounds that Herceptin was unaffordable and too many other patients would suffer. They lost the appeal.

Not all hospitals can afford the more expensive equipment or the necessary trained staff.

Each hospital trust has a limited amount of money to spend. So, sometimes, hard decisions have to be made about which treatments can be given and who will be able to receive them.

Use of techniques

Complete this table

If a technique can be used for diagnosis, therapy and/or for other clinical purposes, include extra rows at the end of the table.

technique	diagnosis	treatment	invasive	non-invasive	used for ...
liquid-in-glass thermometer					
thermistor thermometer					
photochromic thermometer					
sphygmomanometer					
arterial cannula					
electrocardiogram					
electroencephalogram					
X-ray					
alpha (α) particles					
beta (β) particles					
gamma (γ) rays					
ultrasound					
magnetic fields					
thermography					
endoscope					
film badges					
rectilinear scanner					
gamma camera					
radioisotope tracers					
technetium-99m					
iodine-131					
cobalt-60					
iridium-192					
iodine-131					
ultrasound					
laser					
optical fibre					
magnetic resonance imaging					
CAT scan					
PET scan					

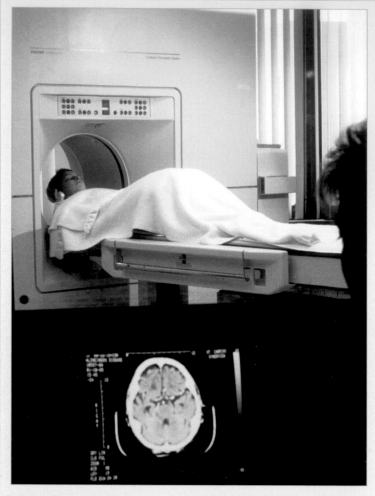

Across:

1 Show whether sections of the brain are functioning correctly.

4 In the cardiac cycle, _____ pressure gives the resting pressure.

6 Used for manual non-invasive blood pressure measurement.

7 Total internal reflection occurs when the angle of incidence to the boundary is greater than the _____ angle.

8 In the cardiac cycle, _____ pressure gives the peak pressure.

9 MRI scans have no known health risks, but they are _____.

10 dose equivalent = absorbed dose x _____ _____.

11 Film badges are a type of _____.

12 X-rays and γ-rays are types of _____ radiation.

14 Body temperature increases to 38 °C or higher.

15 Healthcare professionals who work with X-rays.

17 CAT scans provide better _____ than conventional X-rays for internal organs, bone, soft tissue and blood vessels.

18 This type of thermometer is cheap, but fragile.

19 _____ is often used for shielding because it's good at absorbing radiation.

20 Radioactive decay is _____.

21 A fibre optic camera.

22 Sensitivity of organs to radiation.

24 Brainwave frequency between 8-12 Hz.

25 Transverse waves have peaks and _____.

26 _____ treatment involves the patient being injected with, or swallowing, a radioactive liquid.

27 Can continuously monitor fetal movement or a person's heart.

28 Sound waves are _____ or mechanical.

30 The type of interference when a trough meets a peak.

32 All electromagnetic waves undergo reflection, refraction and _____.

33 MRI scans are used to _____ the brain.

35 When waves decrease in amplitude.

36 A radioisotope that only the thyroid cells pick up.

38 Clinical thermometers have a _____ range of temperatures.

39 Body temperature decreases to 32 °C or lower.

42 Between radio and infrared in the electromagnetic spectrum.

43 Sound waves are longitudinal or _____.

44 PET stands for Positron Emission _____.

45 _____ effects, such as cancer, occur randomly.

46 A γ-ray emitting isotope that is often used as a radioactive tracer.

47 velocity = frequency x _____.

48 The longer the wavelength, the _____ the frequency.

49 Radioactive substances put into the body to aid diagnosis.

50 Material absorbs X-rays and γ-rays depending on its _____ _____.

Down:

1 Heart problems can be located with an _____.

2 The type of interference when two troughs meet.

3 When the heart beats too fast.

5 Has a biological half-life of 18 000 days and an effective half-life of 6800 days.

13 Extreme tiredness, dizziness, fainting and shortness of breath, difficult or painful breathing are symptoms of _____.

16 Doctors who specialise in interpreting X-rays and other types of scans.

19 Therapy often given through a flexible endoscope.

23 There are two main methods for detecting X-rays: _____ and photographic film.

29 A device for counting atomic particles.

31 Type of needle used in invasive arterial blood pressure measuremement.

33 A medical procedure that uses light and optical fibres to look inside the body.

34 36.8 °C is considered _____ body temperature.

37 The _____ half-life is the length of time it takes for the amount of a substance in the body of a living organism to halve.

40 This type of thermometer is easy to read, but it's expensive.

41 A suspension of _____ sulfate can be used when studying the digestion system.

46 There are four types of brainwave: delta, _____, alpha and beta.

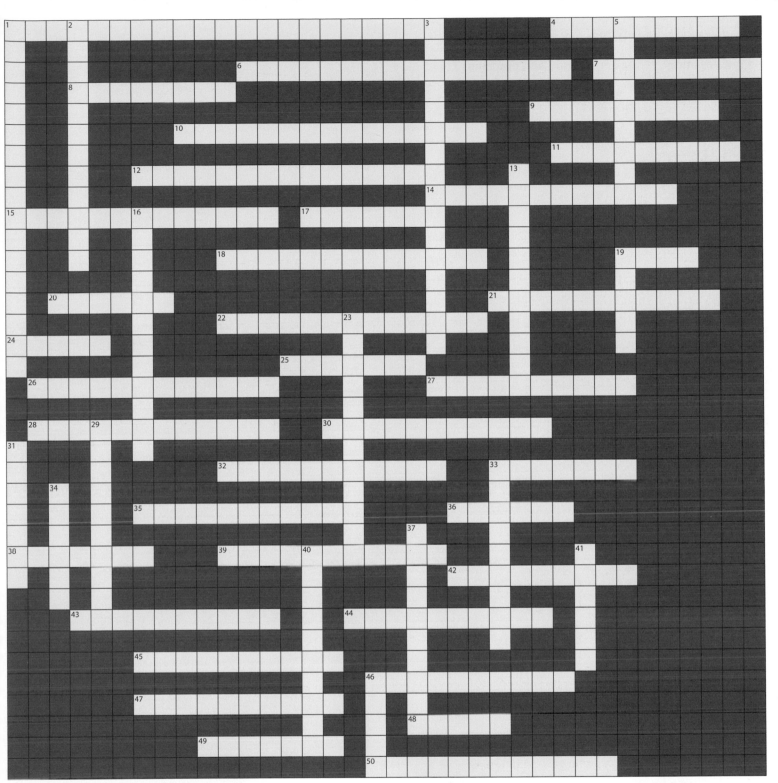

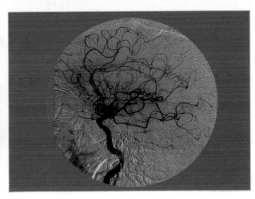

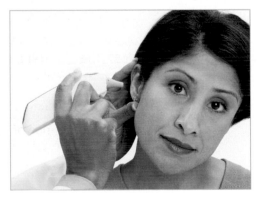

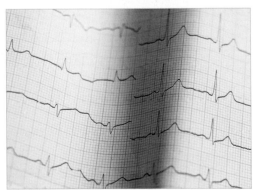

Jot down the key points from your laboratory notes.

investigating	method and outcomes
pulse rate measurement	
blood pressure measurement	
body temperature measurement	
penetrating powers of alpha, beta and gamma radiation	
half-life of a radioisotope measurement	
attenuation of radiation in various materials	
attenuation of sound in various materials	
refractive index measurement	
critical angle measurement	
total internal reflection investigation	
laser light behaviour	
laser light transmission down an optical fibre	
diffraction/attenuation of laser light	

Units, equations and abbreviations

Units

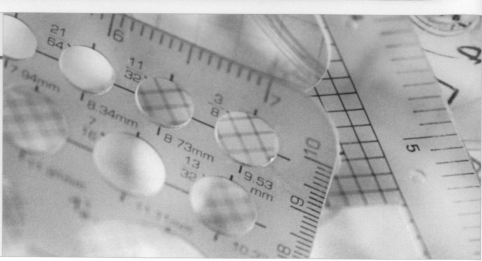

The unit system used here is the International System of Units (SI Units). This is the modern version of the metric system. Although SI is the most commonly used unit system, other unit systems are also used, for example Imperial (units include pints, inches and pounds).

Units named after people start with a lower case letter when written out in full, but a capital when abbreviated.

Units you need to know

quantity	unit	abbreviation
absorbed dose	gray	Gy
distance	metre	m
energy	joule	J
equivalent dose	sievert	Sv
frequency	hertz	Hz
mass	kilogram	kg
(blood) pressure	millimetres of mercury	mm Hg
(blood) pressure	pascal	Pa
radioactivity	becquerel	Bq
speed	metres per second	m s^{-1}
time	seconds	s
temperature	degrees celcius	°C
temperature	kelvin	K

Serious errors

Pay attention to the units and prefixes as mistakes can be serious – sometimes life-threatening.

In 2002 more than 130 breast cancer patients in the west of England were told their cancer may return because they were given the wrong dose of radiotherapy.

And in a Glasgow hospital in 2006, a 15-year old girl was given potentially deadly doses of radiation therapy 17 times when undergoing treatment for a brain tumour.

10% of patients admitted to UK hospitals will be adversely affected by the drugs administered to them.

As well as receiving the wrong drug, there are some other key factors in medical errors:

* wrong dose
* wrong units
* calculation errors (important in paediatrics)
* infusions with incorrect amount of diluent or delivery rate.

Equations

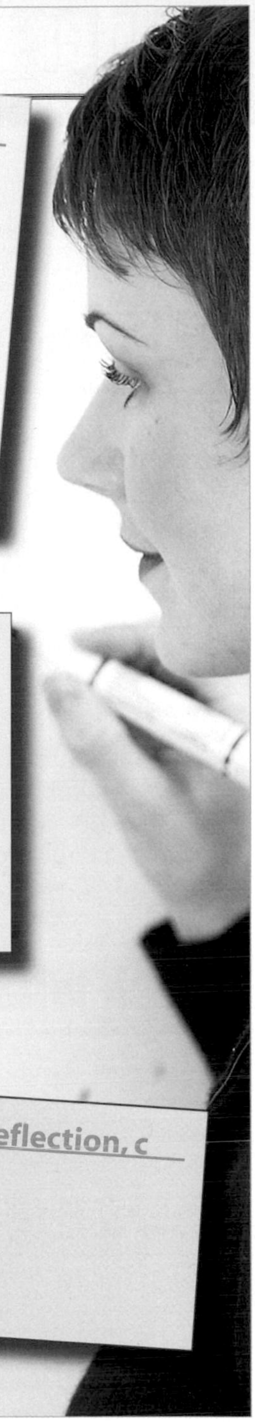

Wave equation

$$v = f\lambda$$

v = velocity (m s^{-1})
f = frequency (Hz)
λ = wavelength (m)

Refraction

n = refractive index
n = velocity of light in air ÷ velocity of light in medium

$$n = \frac{\sin a_i}{\sin a_r}$$

a_i is the angle of incidence
a_r is the angle of refraction

Effective half-life

$$\frac{1}{T_E} = \frac{1}{T_B} + \frac{1}{T_P}$$

T_E = effective half-life
T_B = biological half-life
T_P = physical half-life

Intensity reflection coefficient

for sound waves - between two media

$$\left(\frac{Z_2 - Z_1}{Z_2 + Z_1}\right)^2$$

Inverse square law

$$\frac{I_R}{I_r} = \left(\frac{r}{R}\right)^2$$

I_R = signal intensity at distance R from the source
I_r = signal intensity at distance r from the source

Critical angle for total internal reflection, c

$$\sin c = \frac{1}{n}$$

Abbreviations

ECG	electrocardiogram
EEG	electroencephalogram
MRI	magnetic resonance imaging
CT	computerised tomography
CAT	computed axial tomography
PET	positron emission tomography

Insider information

There's no substitute for sound knowledge and understanding, but students don't always display these as well as they could. Here's some advice from a former examiner on how to tackle the written papers.

Read the question

You can only gain marks by giving the information asked for. What you write may be correct, but if it doesn't answer the question ... no marks.

The exam is about the scientific ideas and techniques that scientists use. The questions don't just test your memory. They're also designed to see whether you can apply the ideas and use information given in the questions.

Make sure you understand:

- what the question is *telling* you
- what the question is *asking* you.

Check the number of marks allocated. These indicate the amount of detail you need to give - at least one piece of information for each mark.

Don't be put off

Some questions are likely to be set in unfamiliar contexts. For example, questions could concern:

- working for a medical instrument manufacturer
- dealing with a road accident.

You may know nothing about the specific topic, but you should know the underlying principles. The question is asking you to apply the principles to a new situation. Any extra information that you need will be given in the question.

Check what you need to do

Here are some common instructions you may meet in exam questions ...

State ...

means you need to recall something that you should have learned.

Describe how ...

or *Explain how ...* means describe the various steps in the process. (*Explain why ...* means give reasons **why** something happens.)

Describe differences between ...

To describe a difference between X and Y, state something about each of them, not just one. For instance, 'X is blue' doesn't show whether you know the colour of Y.

Suggest ...

means you are not expected to know the answer. There may not even be a definite right answer. You must offer ideas that are consistent with the information the question gives you.

Which / what ...?

Which ... normally means you must select your answer from a limited list. Watch out for the singular or plural word that tells you whether you need one answer or more. *What ...* normally requires you to remember the answer, rather than choosing from a list. Unfortunately, question writers don't always stick to these meanings, so make sure you read the questions carefully.

Describe ...

or *Explain ...* requires you to write a sentence or paragraph. Take your cue from the number of marks: [4] means that you must include four important details. Show your understanding by using the correct scientific terminology.

If in doubt, read again

You'll often be required to use information. Any information that you're not expected to know already will always be given in the question.

You may need to go back to the introduction or to a diagram, table or graph to find the information you need.

Show numerical working

A correct answer to a calculation scores full marks. If you show your working, and there is one mistake, you lose only 1 mark, even if your final answer is wrong. However, a wrong answer by itself scores 0.

public domain image

Show what you know

Believe it or not, examiners are on your side.

Questions are designed to help you show how much you understand.

Your answers may not always be what the examiner expected, but if the science is correct and **relevant to the question**, you will earn marks.

Have a go

Don't spend too long struggling with part of a question you can't answer. It could leave you without enough time to complete other questions. Come back to tricky questions later - but **don't leave any unanswered**. You won't lose marks for wrong answers. If you don't know, make a sensible guess. You **might** get 1 mark out of 3, for instance. If you write nothing, you will **definitely** get nothing.

Give yourself the best chance

Organise your revision ...
*   Make a timetable for yourself.
*   Sit in a sensible chair, in a quiet place with good light.
*   Make notes and keep checking what you know.

On the day ...
*   Arrive in good time.
*   Take sharp pencils, several pens, ruler, protractor and calculator.

Be concise

Don't waste time writing unnecessary extra words. Just give clear, short answers.
*   If asked, 'Which hormone controls the glucose level in blood?', just write 'Insulin'. Don't write, 'The level of glucose in the blood is controlled by insulin.'
*   Questions that need longer answers have several lines of answer space. You do not need to fill the space. Give your information in short sentences.
*   Remember, the allocated mark indicates the minimum number of pieces of information you need to give.

And finally

*   Be precise with the terms you use – do you mean *force* or *energy*?
*   The situation given in the question is the one you must write about.
*   Take care when reading graphs and tables.
*   Take care when plotting graphs – and label the axes.
*   Check again that equations balance.
*   Units units units.

1.1 (a) 250 m s^{-1} (b) 1 m (c) 250 Hz

(d) The float will still be at d. Although the energy in the waves travels in the direction of propagation, the particles moving in the wave stay in the same area.

1.2 (a) $3 \times 10^8 \times 60 \times 60 \times 24 \times 365 = 9.46 \times 10^{15}$ m $= 9.46 \times 10^{12}$ km

(b) ~ 8 mins 20 seconds

(c) Each fan stands up immediately after the person next to them stands up. They don't move but a pulse is seen moving around the arena. It is a longitudinal wave.

(d) Sound needs a medium through which it can travel, because it is a mechanical wave; it cannot travel through space.

1.3 velocity = frequency x wavelength = speed of light in a vacuum = 3×10^8 m s^{-1}, frequency = velocity/wavelength

Microwaves: Frequency = $3 \times 10^8 / 10^{-3} = 3 \times 10^{11}$ hertz or Hz

Ultraviolet: Frequency = $3 \times 10^8 / 10^{-9} = 3 \times 10^{17}$ hertz or Hz

They are both minimum frequencies

2.1 (a) 2 mm

(b) 150 GHz.

3.1 (a) To help conduction of heat energy through the glass to the liquid. Glass is a poor conductor of heat.

(b) To enable a quick response to temperature changes, because a small quantity takes less time to warm up or lose heat.

(c) To give even expansion along it, so that the scale has equal sized divisions.

(d) To increase the sensitivity of the thermometer - the scale can have smaller divisions.

(e) The liquid is returned to the bulb by shaking the thermometer, since this liquid was 'trapped' by the narrow constriction.

4.1 Measuring temperature in the rectum gives a more reliable result. Mouth temperature is affected by eating and drinking and the temperature of air breathed in through the mouth.

4.2 By this time the body has lost too much fluid to be able to cool down by sweating and the rising temperature is now causing organ damage.

4.3 Across: 4 hyperthermia 7 urine 8 ear 9 axillary

Down: 1 sweat 2 hypothermia 3 death 5 fever 6 drum

5.1 Any technique that involves entering the body in any way is described as invasive

5.2 (a) The pressure will then reflect the pressure from the heart; it would change if the arm were raised or lowered.

(b) The blood flow is free to flow; this flow is laminar.

(c) These periods represent the turbulent flow of blood when the artery is blocked.

5.3 It may depend on the individual, but likely to have three consecutive rises in systolic pressure followed by a fall, with the highest being caused by your lecturer. Possibly

(a) **128/74** (activity after sleeping causes a rise in systolic pressure)

(b) **130/70** (mildly stressful, systolic pressure rises a bit more but diastolic pressure has fallen a bit as you have not been physically active)

(c) **164/68** (very stressful, heart pumps blood more forcefully so systolic pressure rises)

(d) **149/79** (systolic pressure starts to fall as heart pumps blood at a lower pressure, but diastolic pressure has been raised and takes longer to come down)

6.1

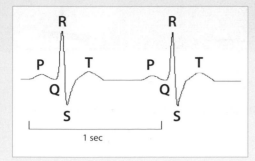

6.2 (a) If they are stressed or active then this would raise the sinus rhythm.

(b) Sinus bradycardia or hypothermia. Look for symptoms of hypothermia.

6.3 Sinus tachycardia = D
Bradycardia = B
Sinus arrhythmia = A
Ventricular fibrillation = C

7.1 (a) a human hand – infrared

(b) a red hot poker – infrared and visible (red light)

7.2 To regulate the body temperature and compensate for any artificially generated heat (outside temperature, car heaters, coats, etc.)

7.3 (a) warmest - red

(b) coolest - blue

7.4 Humans have a body temperature of 310 K, so thermal radiation from humans is highest in the infrared range.

7.5 Across: 2 blood 4 infrared 5 pain 6 risk skin 8 energy
Down: 1 noninvasive 3 quality

8.1 Say: in 100 chlorine atoms, X are chlorine-35 atoms and (100 – X) are chlorine-37 atoms.
So: X atoms have mass 35 and (100 – X) atoms have mass 37. Therefore: 35.5 x 100 = 35X + 37(100 – X)
3550 = 35X + 3700 – 37X
rearranging: 37x – 35x = 3700 – 3550
giving: X = 75
The ratio is 75 atoms of chlorine-35 to 25 atoms of chlorine-37 or 3:1

8.2 (a) They are very powerful ionisers. You would not want to ingest any alpha source because of this. They cause damage to tissues when a source is in close contact.

(b) The total dose equivalent is (50 x 1) + (0.4 x 10) = 54 mSv

(c) (i) Gonads (testicles or ovaries).
(ii) Testicular or ovarian cancer, inability to have children or genetic mutation in offspring.

(d) Different absorption rates in different organs, for different sources of radiation.

8.3

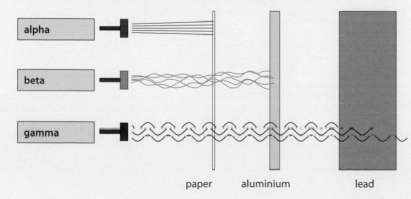

8.4 (a) Beta particles because they are the least ionising.

(b) (i) 192 represents the nucleon number (the number of sub atomic particles that can be found in the nucleus). The total number of protons and neutrons found in the nucleus is 192.

(ii) Since an aplha particle has 2p and 2n, if one is emitted from iridium-192 then the nucleon number will decrease by 2p + 2n = 4, so 192 will reduce to 188.

8.5 After one half-life 1/2 the sample remains (7.3 s).
After two half-lives 1/2 of a 1/2 remains (1/4 after 14.6 s).
After three half-lives 1/2 of a 1/4 remains (1/8 after 21.9 s).
After four half-lives 1/2 of 1/8 remains (1/16 after 29.2 s).
So the fraction that remains is 1/16th.

8.6 three seconds.

9.1 cataracts – deterministic.
leukaemia – stochastic
tumours – stochastic.
sun burn – deterministic

9.2 three centimetres

10.1 (a) The rays at different angles will pass through different areas of healthy tissue, reducing the dose that any area of the healthy tissue receives.

(b) Accurate positioning of the radiotherapy beams is very important. The tattoos can be used to ensure that the beams are always directed in the same place. After treatment they indicate where radiotherapy has taken place.

(c) The images provided by CAT scans can give doctors a much clearer idea of the size and position of the tumour for planning the radiotherapy.

(d) No.

10.2 (a) Yes, although the level of radioactivity will depend on the treatment.

(b) For forms of brachytherapy where the radioactive source is removed after therapy, the patient will no longer be radioactive. For other forms, the radioactivity will fade away according to the half-life of the radioactive substance used.

10.3
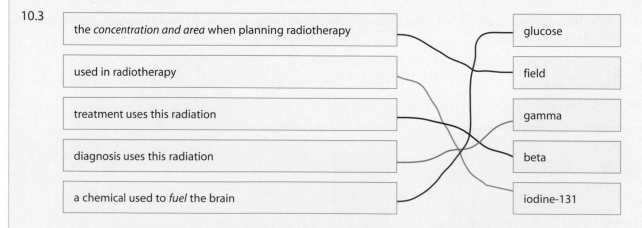

10.4 1/Te = 1/1 + 1/0.2 = 6, so the Effective half-life Te = 1/6

11.1 (a) Physical half-life is the half-life of the radioactive element. Biological half-life refers to the time that the material remains in the body.

(b) four hours

(c) Technetium-99m can be combined into a number of different compounds which target different organs. The biological half-life will depend on how long these organs take to process these compounds.

11.2 It is very penetrative and weakly ionising so it exits the body and does very little damage. Compare this with alpha and beta emitters that are far more ionising.

12.1 velocity = frequency x wavelength, frequency = velocity/wavelength, f = 3x10^8/10^{-10} = 3 x 10^{18} Hz

12.2 Lead has an atomic number of 82, and will therefore be very good at absorbing X-rays.

12.3

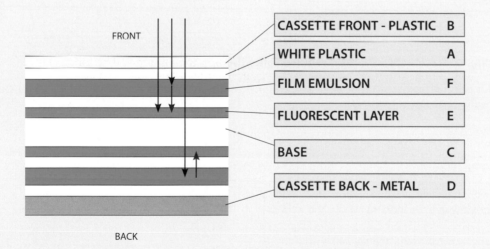

12.4 Electrons are absorbed and scattered by air molecules.

12.5 Increased penetration through an object decreases contrast. The chest has a high contrast primarily because of the air within the lungs.

12.6 (a) Because your bones and teeth are dense and absorb more X-rays than your skin.

(b) Metal absorbs even more X-rays.

13.1 (a) Film position A: **decreasing** distance between object and film sharpens the image

(b) Source position A: **increasing** distance between source and object sharpens the image

13.2

13.3 (a) X-rays and light

(b) X-ray – X-ray tube

Light – X-rays hit the fluorescent screen which converts the X-ray energy into light

(c) Light

(d) Fewer X-rays are needed to produce a good image, reducing the patient's exposure.

13.4 No

14.1 A CAT scan involves much longer exposure to X-rays than conventional X-rays.

14.2 (a) They need to be kept totally still during the examination to prevent blurring of the images.

(b) They physically will struggle to get through the opening.

15.1 (a) Anode will attract the negatively charged electrons that have been *knocked off* the argon atoms and the Cathode will attract the positively charged ions.

(b) The pulse counter is measuring the flow of electrons. A flow of electrons is an electric current.

15.2 Particles only travel a few cm in air so wouldn't physically reach the badge.

15.3 (a) non invasive

(b) organs, tissue and tumours within the body

(c) Gamma cameras detect the radioisotope which will have been taken up differently by different tissues, including tumours.

16.1 (a) Protons in the nucleus are aligned by a magnetic field. Their resonance, when bombarded with radio waves is used to create an image.

(b) The scanner uses an intense magnetic field: the image could be affected; items such as a credit card, could be *wiped*.

(c) The magnetism could move the fragment to a critical location and cause harm.

(d) Scans can take up to an hour. It may lessen the claustrophobic nature of the scanner. Some patients may be unable to lie flat for long periods.

17.1 wavelength = velocity ÷ frequency

Speed of sound ≈ 345 m s⁻¹
at 20 000 Hz:
wavelength = 345 ÷ 20 000 = 0.017 m
at 20 Hz:
wavelength = 345 ÷ 20 = 17 m

17.2 (a) The transducer that produces the ultrasonic waves is placed on the skin using a special gel.

(b) The speed of sound in the gel is part way between that in air and water. It therefore creates a smooth transition for the sound waves resulting in less reflected (wasted) energy.

17.3 (a) skull bone and air

(b) liver and blood

18.1
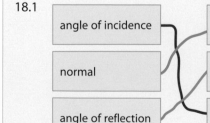

angle of incidence	a construction line at right angles to the surface at the point where the incident ray hits the surface
normal	the angle that the reflected ray makes with the normal, equal to the angle of incidence
angle of reflection	the angle that the incoming ray makes with the normal

18.2 air to glass (no)

glass to air (yes)

diamond to water (yes)

water to glass (no)

water to air (yes)

18.3   (a) (i) 48.8 degrees
           (ii) 24.4 degrees

       (b) boundary from air to water: incident angle is greater than critical angle – total internal reflection will occur

           boundary from diamond to air: incident angle is 15° – less than critical angle – total internal reflection will not occur

18.4

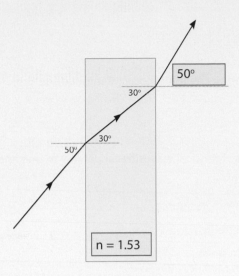

18.5   (a)

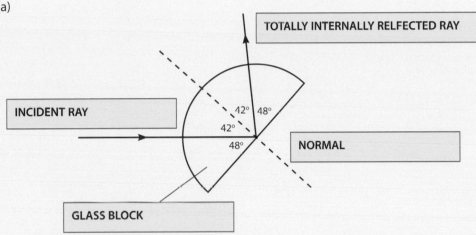

       (b) The direction of the light is along a normal.

       (c) In this case, the direction of the ray is deviated **away** from the normal. Total internal reflection happens when the direction of the ray would deviate so much that it wouldn't make it into the material with the lower refractive index. When the ray moves from a lower to a higher refractive index, the direction deviates **towards** the normal.

19.1

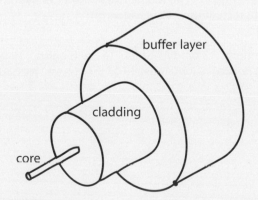

19.2   Light rays would pass between fibres at the points of contact. As a result, the fibres would become uniformly bright so no image would be formed.

Answers

19.3　(a) multimode; step index

　　　(b) multimode; graded index

　　　(c) single mode; step index

19.4　(a) A biopsy is a *sample* that is sliced away using a cutting instrument attached to the endoscope (manipulator).

　　　(b) Infection, punctured organs.

20.1　(a) White light is a mix of colours with mixed wavelengths.

　　　(b) Laser light is monochromatic with a single wavelength. It is coherent. These identical waves travel parallel to one another.

　　　(c) Laser light travels as a tight beam.

　　　(d) Ordinary light spreads out so less light hits a given area as it travels away from its source.

　　　(e) The strong parallel laser beam can be focused to a few micrometres in diameter.

　　　(f) Laser light can be controlled precisely, in a continuous beam, in bursts or in pulses.

20.2　The red light is at the correct frequency to activate the drug.

20.3　**Advantages**

　　　No large incisions needed

　　　Avoids open surgery and the resulting scar

　　　Shorter hospital stay

　　　Less pain

　　　Shorter convalescence

　　　Disadvantages

　　　More often a longer operation

　　　Loss of tactile information

　　　Bleeding infection at the 'port' site

　　　Higher level of skill required by the surgeon

Giant crossword

Across:　1 electroencephalograms　4 diastolic　6 sphygmonometer　7 critical　8 systolic　9 expensive　10 weighting factor　11 dosimeter　12 electromagnetic　14 hyperthermia　15 radiographers　17 clarity　18 liquid in glass　19 lead　20 random　21 laparascope　22 organ affinity　24 alpha　25 troughs　26 radioisotope　27 ultrasound　28 longitudinal　30 destructive　32 diffraction　33 examine　35 attenuation　36 iodine　38 limited　39 hypothermia　42 microwave　43 mechanical　44 tomography　45 stochastic　46 technitium　47 wavelength　48 lower　49 tracers　50 atomic number

Down:　1 electrocardiogram　2 constructive　3 sinus tachycardia　5 strontium　13 bradychardia　16 radiologists　19 laser　23 fluorescence　29 geiger tube　31 cannula　33 endoscopy　34 normal　37 biological　40 thermistor　41 barium　46 theta

Your notes

Your glossary